The Great American Trivia Quiz Book

An All-American Trivia Book to
Test Your General Knowledge!

BILL O'NEILL

ISBN: 978-1-64845-061-7

DON'T FORGET YOUR FREE BOOKS

CONTENTS

CHAPTER 1

INTRODUCTION

The United States, home to 329 million people living in 50 states, has a rich history made up of so much more than just its presidents and wars. From the women who disguised themselves as men to fight in the Civil War, to the story of jazz music, this book delves into the history of Americans beyond the rich, white men to include women, children, African Americans, and the poor.

The many people who have immigrated to the United States, from the first colony at Jamestown to the present, have enriched American culture. The United States is truly a nation of immigrants, and that diversity is reflected in the nation's food, music, arts, films, and traditions. This book tells you everything you ever wanted to know about the life of Americans, including all the different types of American barbeque, the most popular music festivals, and even the ostrich races! We have done our best to include all voices and regions in this text.

Not only is the United States a diverse society, geographically it has some of the most varied and beautiful landscapes in the world. Home to rainforests, deserts, mountains, and seas, virtually every type of landscape can be found in this large country, and the scenery often changes quickly from state to state. This book explores lesser-known places and the creatures that live there, like the Great Sand Dunes National Park in Colorado and the bizarre-looking elephant seal that can be found on the Point Reyes National Seashore in California.

Hollywood has fascinated the world since its inception and it still dominates the film industry today. Most people know Hollywood's most famous actors and actresses, but do you know where the code from *The Matrix* came from or in how many countries *Game of Thrones* was filmed? Get ready to find out some fun, minute details from famous movies and TV shows from the past to the present in these pages.

Every country has its fair share of urban legends and unexplained events, and the United States has way too many to count. Who was the Zodiac Killer? What presidential ghost haunts the White House? Were there *really* vampires in New Orleans? Learn the facts, the myths, and the mysteries of American history in this trivia book.

Americans spend a shocking amount of time watching sports. The United States has so many talented players and teams who play football, hockey, basketball, and who ski and snowboard—just to name a few of their many sporting endeavors. Everyone has heard of the famous baseball player, Babe Ruth, but most people do not know what vegetable he always wore under his hat. Read on to find out!

This book will test your trivia knowledge about the United States and teach you tons of fun new facts. From baseball and the blues to Hollywood, there are so many interesting things that are uniquely American. Each chapter of this book contains a quiz, an answer key, and a 'Did You Know?' section filled with entertaining and random facts. Most of the information is organized chronologically, except for chapters focused on specific niche topics, like food and music.

After you are done reading this book, you will be sure to impress your friends and win every trivia game, whether it is played at home or your local bar!

CHAPTER 2

LIFE IN EARLY
AMERICA QUIZ

1. Who was the first European explorer, since the Norsemen, to set foot in North America in 1497?

   a. Christopher Columbus
   b. John Cabot
   c. John Smith
   d. Chris Hudson

2. When Columbus arrived in the Americas, according to some estimates, roughly how many Native Americans were living in what is now the United States?

   a. 2.5 million
   b. 500,000
   c. 1.5 million
   d. 3 million

3. What type/s of house/s did Native Americans live in during colonial times?

   a. Igloos
   b. Rectangular Plank Houses

   c. Tepees

   d. All of the above

4. What was the name of the French Protestants who settled in modern-day Florida long before the English arrived?

   a. French Canadians

   b. Huguenots

   c. Floridians

   d. New French

5. Which devastating disease, brought over from Europe, ravaged the Native American population in the Americas?

   a. Scarlet fever

   b. Smallpox

   c. Tuberculosis

   d. Cancer

6. Captive Africans were likely present in the Americas in the 1400s and as early as 1526 in the present-day United States.

   a. True

   b. False

7. Which famous explorer landed near the present-day city of St. Augustine, Florida in 1513?

   a. Christopher Columbus

   b. Juan Ponce de León

   c. John Cabot

   d. John Smith

8. What was the name of the first permanent English settlement founded in the United States in 1607?

    a. Roanoke

    b. Salem

    c. Jamestown

    d. Hudson

9. What colony was founded by James Oglethorpe as a place for British citizens who were in debtors' prisons?

    a. Pennsylvania

    b. Georgia

    c. Virginia

    d. Maryland

10. What was the name of the group of people who founded the Massachusetts Bay colony called "the city upon a hill"?

    a. Catholics

    b. Mormons

    c. Puritans

    d. Reformers

11. Mississippi was the first state to legalize slavery, and Massachusetts was the last state to officially abolish slavery.

    a. True

    b. False

12. In the year 1640, the trend of emigration from England to Massachusetts reversed. Puritans started sailing to England

to fight for the Parliamentarians instead of emigrating to America.

   a. True

   b. False

13. In what colony did the Salem witch trials take place?

   a. Roanoke

   b. Jamestown

   c. Massachusetts Bay Colony

   d. New York Colony

14. Which famous play depicts the Salem Witch Trials?

   a. Trouble in Salem

   b. The Crucible

   c. Witches on Trial

   d. The Devil in Salem

15. In which way were those accused of witchcraft in the Salem Witch Trials punished?

   a. Hanged

   b. Burned at the stake

   c. Put in jail

   d. Starved to death

16. Despite working hard all day and wearing the same clothes most of the time, colonial farmers very seldom bathed or washed.

   a. True

   b. False

17. Who founded the city of Philadelphia, also known as the "city of brotherly love"?

    a. William Philadelphia

    b. William Penn

    c. Sir Walter Raleigh

    d. James I

18. Because of the shortage in official English coins, colonists often bought and sold items with what?

    a. Tobacco

    b. Gin

    c. Land

    d. Pigs

19. In 1691, Virginia was the first colony to criminalize interracial marriage, passing the first law to restrict access to marriage partners based on race alone. All bans on interracial marriage in the United States were finally lifted in what year?

    a. 1865

    b. 1920

    c. 1955

    d. 1967

20. Remarriages were extremely uncommon in Colonial America.

    a. True

    b. False

ANSWER KEY

1. B- John Cabot

2. C- 1.5 million

3. D- All of the above

4. B- Huguenots

5. B- Smallpox

6. A- True

7. B- Juan Ponce de León

8. C- Jamestown

9. B- Georgia

10. C- Puritans

11. B- False

12. A- True

13. C- Massachusetts Bay Colony

14. B- The Crucible

15. A- Hanged

16. A- True

17. B- William Penn

18. A- Tobacco

19. D- 1967

20. B- False

DID YOU KNOW?

1. In 1540, Spanish explorer Francisco Coronado ended up in the Grand Canyon and Kansas on his mission to search for the mythical Seven Golden Cities of Cíbola. On their journey, Coronado's teams' horses escaped and forever changed life on the Great Plains. Native Americans in the Plains became excellent horseback riders and were able to travel much further than ever before.

2. In 1587, a group of 115 English settlers arrived on Roanoke Island, off the coast of North Carolina. The governor of the colony, John White, had to sail back to England and when he returned in 1590, all the colony's inhabitants, including his wife and daughter, had vanished. The most mysterious part of their disappearance is that they left no trace except for a single word, "Croatoan," which was carved into a wooden post. What is now known as the "Lost Colony" of Roanoke remains a mystery to this day.

3. Pocahontas was more than just a Disney character; she was the Native American daughter of Chief Powhatan. Her uncle captured Captain John Smith, who lived in the Jamestown Colony. John Smith wrote about being saved by Pocahontas during his time in captivity, but the facts of their story are still debated by historians.

4. Most people envision life in early America to be "proper" and would not think that premarital sex was common.

Believe it or not, many people were sharing beds before marriage in colonial times. In the second half of the 1700s, at least one in three women were pregnant when they got married.

5. It was a harsh reality in Colonial America that parents expected children to die. Four in ten children died before age 6.

6. In 1758, loud noises woke up the residents of Windham, Connecticut and they thought they were under attack by the Native Americans. They armed themselves and headed toward the noise, but all they discovered was thousands of frogs fighting over the water in the town pond; there was little of it as they were experiencing a drought. This became known as "The Battle of the Frogs."

7. Mobs in early America often tarred and feathered people to exact justice or revenge. The victim would be stripped naked and wood tar would be poured or painted onto them. They would then have feathers thrown at them or be rolled around on a pile of feathers, which would stick to the tar.

8. The word "Indian" came from Christopher Columbus and his incorrect belief that he had landed on the shores of South Asia. He used the term "Indios" meaning "person from the Indus valley" to describe the native people in the Americas.

9. Women in colonial times often had one primary goal: to get married as soon as possible. Women often married

when they were noticeably young, and it was not usually for love.

10. The lower classes in Colonial America liked playing a game called "Put," which was an early version of poker.

CHAPTER 3

THE CREATION OF A NEW NATION AND WESTERN EXPLORATION QUIZ

1. In December 1773, the Sons of Liberty dressed up as Indians and threw 342 chests of what into the Boston Harbor to protest taxes?

    a. Tobacco
    b. Gin
    c. Cash
    d. Tea

2. Who was the British King during the American Revolutionary War?

    a. King James I
    b. King George III
    c. King Thomas IV
    d. King George I

3. The French government supplied the American rebels with arms, ammunition, and cash throughout the American Revolutionary War.

    a. True

b. False

4. How many American colonies fought for their independence in the American Revolutionary War?

   a. 15

   b. 10

   c. 11

   d. 13

5. An estimated number of 3,000 freed slaves fought on both sides during the American Revolutionary War.

   a. True

   b. False

6. On what holiday did George Washington famously cross the icy Delaware River to New Jersey to surprise the enemy forces?

   a. Christmas

   b. Halloween

   c. Thanksgiving

   d. The 4th of July

7. After the Battle of Germantown during the American Revolutionary War, General George Washington returned what to General William Howe after the battle?

   a. His sword

   b. His hat

   c. His dog

   d. His horse

8. There was a secret attempt to remove which person as the

commander-in-chief during the American Revolutionary War?

   a. General George Washington

   b. General Patrick Henry

   c. General Thomas Conway

   d. General Benjamin Franklin

9. Which side was referred to as the Redcoats during the American Revolutionary War?

   a. The British

   b. The Colonists

   c. The Spanish

   d. The French

10. Who was the British commander during the American Revolutionary War?

   a. General John Smith

   b. General William Howe

   c. General James I

   d. General Tom Sprout

11. Where did the British surrender the war?

   a. Yorktown

   b. Gettysburg

   c. Vicksburg

   d. Salem

12. What was the name of the treaty that ended the American Revolutionary War?

   a. Treaty of Versailles

b. Treaty of the Americas

c. Treaty of Berlin

d. Treaty of Paris

13. Which body served as the government of the 13 American colonies, and the United States of America, from 1774–1789?

   a. Gang of 13

   b. The Founding Fathers

   c. Continental Congress

   d. Sons of Liberty

14. Which important document preceded the United States Constitution?

   a. The Articles of Confederation

   b. The Emancipation Proclamation

   c. The Bill of the Independent

   d. None of the above

15. Thomas Jefferson was clearly not busy enough drafting the Declaration of Independence because he took time out to invent (purportedly) which modern-day item?

   a. Telephone

   b. Swivel chair

   c. Clock

   d. Sled

16. What was the name of the Native American woman who met the explorers Meriwether Lewis and William Clark, and became the translator for their famous voyage across

the United States?

   a. Pocahontas

   b. Little Feather

   c. Sacagawea

   d. Pine Leaf

17. Which United States president tasked Meriwether Lewis with taking an expedition to explore the lands west of the Mississippi in 1804?

   a. George Washington

   b. Thomas Jefferson

   c. George Bush

   d. Martin Van Buren

18. How far did Lewis and Clark travel on their journey gathering information about uncharted territory in North America?

   a. 10,000 miles

   b. 2,000 miles

   c. 18,000 miles

   d. 8,000 miles

19. Thomas Jefferson, as intelligent as he was, was convinced that Lewis and Clark would encounter what on their expedition?

   a. Wooly mammoths

   b. Giant ground sloths

   c. Mountains of salt

   d. All of the above

20. Historians estimate that six to seven million enslaved African Americans were taken to the New World in the 18th century.

    a. True
    b. False

ANSWER KEY

1. D- Tea
2. B- King George III
3. A- True
4. D- 13
5. B- False, an estimated 25,000 freed Black slaves fought on both sides
6. A- Christmas
7. C- His dog
8. A- General George Washington
9. A- British
10. B- General William Howe
11. A- Yorktown
12. D- Treaty of Paris
13. C- Continental Congress
14. A- The Articles of Confederation
15. B- Swivel chair
16. C- Sacagawea
17. B- Thomas Jefferson
18. D- 8,000 miles
19. D- All of the above
20. A- True

DID YOU KNOW?

1. The Boston Tea Party was not a one-time occurrence. In 1774, they did it again, except instead of dumping 342 chests of tea, they dumped 30.

2. Everyone has heard of Paul Revere, but few have heard of Sybil Ludington. At the age of 16, Sybil, the daughter of a colonel, rode her horse for 40 miles all night by herself, on roads she was unfamiliar with, to alert New York militia that the British were burning Danbury, Connecticut.

3. There are multiple copies of the Declaration of Independence. The copies are known as the "Dunlap Broadsides" and it is estimated that 26 copies remain.

4. The Declaration of Independence was only signed by one person on July 4, 1776. More than a month went by before the actual signing took place.

5. One of the members of the committee who wrote the Declaration of Independence, Robert Livingston, refused to sign it.

6. Benjamin Franklin had to be carried in a sedan chair to the Constitutional Convention by prisoners from the Walnut Street Jail.

7. The founding father of Delaware, Caesar Rodney, is depicted on Delaware's state quarter, but historians have no idea what he looked like. Rodney always covered his face up with a cloth because he had severe facial cancer.

8. In 1794, there was an uprising of farmers and distillers in Pennsylvania who were protesting a whiskey tax instituted by the federal government. The uprising became known as "the Whiskey Rebellion."

9. In 1838, government authorities forced Cherokee Native Americans from their homes and held them at gunpoint on a journey of over 1,200 miles by foot. They moved them to "Indian Territory" which is now in Oklahoma. More than 4,000 people died on the journey now known as "The Trail of Tears."

10. For a long time, tomatoes were considered a poisonous fruit; a surgeon, John Gerard, deemed them poisonous because they contained very small amounts of the toxin called tomatine. Additionally, the fruit was red and considered to be "sinful" because of its aphrodisiac properties. In 1820, tomatoes were put on trial in the town's courthouse in Salem, New Jersey. Colonel Robert Gibbon Johnson ate an entire basketful of tomatoes in front of the crowd. After the crowd observed that he was fine, the tomato's reputation as being toxic ceased and it became a popular item to be grown in every garden.

CHAPTER 4

THE CIVIL WAR AND RECONSTRUCTION QUIZ

1. The Civil War in the United States was fought during what years?

    a. 1850–1855
    b. 1825–1830
    c. 1861–1865
    d. 1770–1775

2. The first shots of the Civil War were fired where?

    a. Fort Sumter
    b. Gettysburg
    c. Richmond
    d. Shiloh

3. Which Civil War battle is considered the bloodiest day in all of American history?

    a. Battle of Gettysburg
    b. Battle of Antietam
    c. Battle of Bull Run
    d. Battle of Vicksburg

4. Within three months of the election of which president did seven states—Mississippi, Alabama, South Carolina, Florida, Georgia, Louisiana, and Texas—secede from the United States in November of 1860?

    a. President Andrew Jackson
    b. President Ulysses S. Grant
    c. President Abraham Lincoln
    d. President James Buchanan

5. New York City considered seceding from the Union to form the republic of "Tri-Insula."

    a. True
    b. False

6. _____ was a surgeon and volunteered for the Union Army until her capture by Confederate forces. She was held as a prisoner of war in Richmond, Virginia. After the war, she was awarded the Medal of Honor, making her the only woman in U.S. history to ever receive it.

    a. Mary Edwards Walker
    b. Belle Boyd
    c. Harriet Tubman
    d. Pocahontas

7. Which famous document, signed by President Abraham Lincoln on January 1, 1863, declared that "All persons held as slaves within any State…in rebellion against the United States, shall be then, thenceforward, and forever free…"?

a. The Declaration of Independence
b. The Constitution
c. The Emancipation Proclamation
d. The Declaration of Rights and Sentiments

8. The Civil War was the deadliest in American history.

   a. True
   b. False

9. Approximately how many women disguised themselves as men to fight in the Civil War?

   a. 10
   b. 150
   c. 75
   d. 400

10. _____was a famous nurse during the Civil War, nicknamed the "Angel of the Battlefields." After the Civil War, she founded the Red Cross.

    a. Mary Todd Lincoln
    b. Virginia Lee
    c. Clara Barton
    d. Harriet Beecher Stowe

11. Who served as the President of the Confederate States of America throughout the Civil War?

    a. Abraham Lincoln
    b. Jefferson Davis
    c. Robert E. Lee
    d. Stonewall Jackson

12. Native Americans served for both the Union and the Confederacy during the Civil War.

    a. True
    b. False

13. How many men died during the Civil War (including both Union and Confederate troops)?

    a. Approximately one million
    b. Approximately 200,000
    c. Approximately 510,000
    d. Approximately 620,000

14. Which Union Army general later went on to become the President of the United States?

    a. John Buford
    b. Grover Cleveland
    c. Ulysses S. Grant
    d. Harry Truman

15. Which amendment granted Black men the right to vote?

    a. 13th Amendment
    b. 16th Amendment
    c. 12th Amendment
    d. 15th Amendment

16. The 20 years after the Civil War was known as what?

    a. The Reconstruction Era
    b. The Reconciliation Era
    c. The Antebellum Period
    d. The Restoration Era

17. What was the purpose of the Freedmen's Bureau?

    a. To take land from white landowners and give it to freed slaves
    b. To provide aid to newly freed African Americans to help them transition from slavery to freedom
    c. To punish Southern states
    d. To help freed slaves run for political office

18. Who assassinated President Abraham Lincoln on April 14, 1865, in Washington, D.C.?

    a. Robert E. Lee
    b. John Jones
    c. John Wilkes Booth
    d. Lee Harvey Oswald

19. What was the purpose of the Black Codes enacted in almost all southern states in 1865 and 1866?

    a. Provide freed slaves with jobs
    b. Teach freed slaves to read
    c. To help freed slaves gain economic freedom
    d. To restrict freed slaves' labor opportunities

20. What were white Southerners who supported Reconstruction after the Civil War called?

    a. Nincompoops
    b. Scalawags
    c. Rapscallions
    d. Villains

ANSWER KEY

1. C- 1861 to 1865

2. A- Fort Sumter

3. B- Battle of Antietam

4. C- President Abraham Lincoln

5. A- True

6. A- Mary Edwards Walker

7. C- The Emancipation Proclamation

8. A- True

9. D- 300

10. C- Clara Barton

11. B- Jefferson Davis

12. A- True

13. D- Approximately 620,000

14. C- Ulysses S. Grant

15. D- 15th Amendment

16. A- The Reconstruction Era

17. B- To provide aid to newly freed African Americans to help them transition from slavery to freedom

18. C- John Wilkes Booth

19. D- To restrict freed slaves' labor opportunities

20. B- Scalawags

DID YOU KNOW?

1. A woman who was disguised as a soldier gave birth to a baby at the Civil War Camp at Johnson's Island in Ohio. A local newspaper wrote about a "strange birth" in the Confederate Army. The newspaper, the *Commercial Register*, claimed that a prisoner gave birth to a baby boy, stating "This is the first instance of a father giving birth to a child that we have heard of."

2. Andersonville Prison Camp, officially named Camp Sumter, was the most notorious Civil War prison camp. Open for less than two years, the prison camp had a death toll of 13,000 Union prisoners. The commander of the camp, Captain Henry Wirz, was convicted and executed for war crimes after the war.

3. During the Civil War, after the Battle of Shiloh, soldiers reported that they had glow-in-the-dark battle wounds. The mysterious light blue glow became known as "Angel's Glow" because the soldiers who had glowing wounds were more likely to survive. Two Maryland teenagers solved the mystery in 2001. The wounded soldiers lay in the cold battlefield waiting to be treated for so long that their bodies became hypothermic. Their low body temperatures provided the necessary conditions for a bioluminescent bacterium to thrive.

4. Everyone knows Abraham Lincoln as "Honest Abe," but

besides honesty, he had other qualities that are not as well known. He was known for his good sense of humor and boisterous banter.

5. Immigrants made up one-third of the soldiers who fought for the Union.

6. Edward Black was the youngest Civil War soldier: he was just 8 years old when he joined the Union army as a drummer boy. He served for the 21st Indiana volunteers. The drum that he used can now be found at the Children's Museum of Indianapolis.

7. Confederate General Thomas J. "Stonewall" Jackson was shot by his own troops in the Battle of Chancellorsville and died a few days later. Who shot Stonewall Jackson? Nobody knows. Although, it is believed that the general died from pneumonia, not his wounds. What is known is his death had a profound impact on the Civil War.

8. The Congressional Medal of Honor was awarded to 25 Black soldiers for their bravery in the Civil War.

9. White Southerners who joined the Republican Party and helped with the Reconstruction were called "scalawags," which was the name originally given to describe "worthless farm animals."

10. President Andrew Johnson became president after Abraham Lincoln. His nickname was "the Tennessee Tailor" because of his career before politics as a tailor.

CHAPTER 5

THE ROARING TWENTIES

1. What were journalists and novelists who exposed corruption in government and big business called?

    a. Vigilantes
    b. Muckrakers
    c. Private eyes
    d. Secret exposers

2. In what year were women in the United States granted the right to vote in national elections after over a decade of fighting for suffrage?

    a. 1870
    b. 1920
    c. 1915
    d. 1895

3. Which famous author wrote the iconic Jazz Age novel, *The Great Gatsby*?

    a. Ernest Hemingway
    b. Langston Hughes
    c. F. Scott Fitzgerald

d. Duke Ellington

4. Who opened the first birth control clinic in the United States in 1916 and the second birth control clinic in 1923?

    a. Alice Paul
    b. Margaret Sanger
    c. Ella Fitzgerald
    d. Elizabeth Cady Stanton

5. A young high school teacher, John Scopes, was placed on trial in 1925 for violating state law by teaching what subject matter?

    a. Sex education for high school students, both male and female
    b. The injustices of the Jim Crow Laws, particularly, the barbaric nature of the miscegenation law
    c. Jazz music theory
    d. Darwin's theory of evolution

6. Which Constitutional amendment banned the production, importation, transportation, and sale of alcohol?

    a. 18th Amendment
    b. 15th Amendment
    c. 19th Amendment
    d. 13th Amendment

7. What famous novel, written in the 1920s by Upton Sinclair, highlighted the horrific conditions of the meatpacking industry in America?

    a. The Jungle

b. The Meatpacking Disaster of the 1920s

c. Labor in NYC

d. A Tale of Two Cities

8. What were the young women called who embraced lifestyle choices like smoking, drinking, dancing, wearing shorter dresses, and experiencing sexual freedom?

a. Dancers

b. It Girls

c. Flappers

d. Jazzies

9. How did the speakeasies of the 1920s get their name?

a. Customers who entered speakeasies had to whisper code words to enter

b. It was easy to speak after drinking alcohol, especially after drinking absinthe, which was quite common in the 1920s

c. It was believed that people who drank a lot talked too much

d. There is no known history on the origination of the word

10. Which infamous "gangster" made millions in liquor sales during prohibition?

a. J. Edgar Hoover

b. Clyde Barrow

c. Tony Soprano

d. Al Capone

11. The Ku Klux Klan was a strong advocate of prohibition.

    a. True
    b. False

12. On December 5, 1933, the 21st Amendment was ratified, and prohibition was officially over. What is the name of this day?

    a. Liquor Day
    b. Repeal Day
    c. Let's Drink Day
    d. National Alcohol Day

13. People who consumed bathtub gin and moonshine during Prohibition risked being poisoned.

    a. True
    b. False

14. What were the alcohol smugglers' ships called during Prohibition?

    a. Rumrunners
    b. Pirate ships
    c. Bootleggers
    d. Fishing boats

15. What drew some of the greatest African American artists and intellectuals of the time to Harlem in New York City?

    a. High paying jobs
    b. The Great Migration
    c. The end of slavery
    d. The Great Depression

16. Who was a famous author during the Harlem Renaissance?

    a. Zora Neale Hurston
    b. Langston Hughes
    c. Claude McKay
    d. All of the above

17. By 1920, more than 175,000 African Americans had moved to Harlem and it had become the largest concentration of Black people in the world.

    a. True
    b. False

18. What type of music that came out of the Harlem Renaissance shaped America?

    a. Country
    b. R&B
    c. Soul
    d. Jazz

19. What was one of the most important inventions of the 1920s that is still important today?

    a. Penicillin
    b. Potato Chips
    c. Baseball
    d. Telephone

20. The American economy was booming in the 1920s and the mass production of goods finally made what products available to the average family?

a. Automobiles
b. Radios
c. Phonographs
d. All of the above

ANSWER KEY

1. B- Muckrakers

2. B- 1920

3. C- F. Scott Fitzgerald

4. B- Margaret Sanger

5. D- Darwin's theory of evolution

6. A- 18th Amendment

7. A- The Jungle

8. C- Flappers

9. A- Customers who entered speakeasies had to whisper code words to enter

10. D- Al Capone

11. A- True

12. B- Repeal Day

13. A- True

14. A- Rumrunners

15. B- The Great Migration

16. D- All of the above

17. A- True

18. D- Jazz

19. A- Penicillin

20. D- All of the above

DID YOU KNOW?

1. It was never illegal to drink during prohibition. The 18th Amendment banned the manufacturing, sale, and distribution of liquor, but not the consumption of it. People continued drinking, but they had to purchase alcohol illegally.

2. The modern concept of booze cruises began during Prohibition. Ships would cruise out to international waters where they could legally serve alcohol on what they called "cruises to nowhere." They would cruise around in circles with no destination in mind.

3. There was only one way to get alcohol legally and that was at the drugstore with a prescription from a physician. Doctors typically prescribed whiskey or brandy and had to fill out the prescription on government prescription forms.

4. Tainted alcohol is estimated to have killed more than 10,000 people before Prohibition finally ended. Additionally, an illegal and toxic brew of alcohol called the "Ginger Jake," created by a pair of men in Boston, crippled up to 100,000 people across the United States.

5. One of the major advocates of Prohibition, the Women's Christian Temperance Union (WCTU), told people it was a scientific fact that beer drinkers die from edema, which is the swelling of the organs or body.

6. The unassuming islands of Saint Pierre and Miquelon, off the coast of Newfoundland, ended up serving as the United States' liquor warehouse during Prohibition. Alcohol would be loaded onto smugglers' ships and sailed to the "rum line," which was located just past the United States three-mile territorial line. They would anchor their ships at the spot that became known as "rum row."

7. The Harlem Renaissance, also known as the "New Negro Movement," blossomed in the 1920s and provided a foundation for the Civil Rights Movement.

8. Automobiles became so affordable in the 1920s that the Ford Model T cost only $260 in 1924.

9. The people who made, imported, and/or sold alcohol during prohibition were called "bootleggers." The name is said to have originated from the practice of American frontiersmen who carried illegal bottles of alcohol in the tops of their boots.

10. The Roaring Twenties ended with the stock market crash on October 29, 1929—also known as "Black Tuesday"—when the Great Depression began.

CHAPTER 6

WORLD WAR I AND WORLD WAR II QUIZ

1. Although World War I started in July of 1914, the United States did not enter the war until what year?

    a. 1915
    b. 1916
    c. 1917
    d. 1918

2. Who was the President of the United States during World War I?

    a. President Woodrow Wilson
    b. President Theodore Roosevelt
    c. President William Howard Taft
    d. President William Harding

3. Women picketed the White House during World War I, accusing the President of the United States of fighting for democracy abroad when American women were not free.

    a. True
    b. False

4. Which act, passed in the United States, authorized the conscription of men for the military, so the nation did not have to rely only on volunteers to fight in World War I?

    a. The Draft Act of 1917
    b. The Selective Service Act of 1917
    c. The Allies Act of 1917
    d. The Conscription Act of 1917

5. Did some African Americans from the United States fight in World War I willingly, despite the segregation they faced on the home front?

    a. Yes
    b. No
    c. African Americans were drafted but they did not volunteer to join the military

6. During World War I, German immigrants, Americans who had German heritage, and those who spoke German were all targets of xenophobic comments, discrimination, and violence.

    a. True
    b. False

7. How many professionally trained female nurses did the American Red Cross recruit to serve in the army between 1917 to 1919?

    a. 10,000
    b. 12,000
    c. 17,000
    d. 22,000

8. What was the name of the treaty that officially ended World War I?

    a. Treaty of Paris

    b. Treaty of Versailles

    c. Treaty of the World

    d. Treaty of Berlin and Russia

9. When was the surprise attack launched by the Japanese at Pearl Harbor, the United States naval base near Honolulu, Hawaii?

    a. December 7, 1941

    b. October 1, 1940

    c. September 5, 1941

    d. January 1, 1942

10. During World War II, the United States detonated two nuclear bombs over which two Japanese cities?

    a. Tokyo and Nagasaki

    b. Hiroshima and Nagasaki

    c. Osaka and Kyoto

    d. Hiroshima and Yokohama

11. President Franklin Roosevelt ordered the establishment of Japanese internment camps during World War II. Japanese and Japanese Americans, primarily from the West Coast of the United States, were exiled to the internment camps until the end of the war.

    a. True

    b. False

12. How many American women served in the United States Armed Forces abroad and at home during World War II?

    a. 150,000
    b. 225,000
    c. 295,000
    d. 350,000

13. What was the name of the cultural icon that encouraged women to go to work during World War II and came to represent the many women who produced munitions and war supplies?

    a. Rose the River Otter
    b. Rosie the Riveter
    c. Madeline the Machine
    d. Mary the Mad

14. How many people of Japanese ancestry were exiled to Japanese Internment Camps during World War II?

    a. 120,000
    b. 55,000
    c. 35,000
    d. 85,000

15. How many American casualties were there during World War II?

    a. 101,502
    b. 352,530
    c. 291,557
    d. 172,353

16. Who was the youngest serviceman to serve in the United States military during World War II?

    a. Calvin Leon Graham, age 12

    b. Joseph Harris, age 12

    c. Thomas Smith, age 12

    d. John Thomas III, age 12

17. The Americans were so anti-German during World War II that they did not even want to use the word "hamburger" because they thought it sounded too German. Instead, they used the word "Liberty Steak."

    a. True

    b. False

18. How many sheets of toilet paper a day did American troops receive as part of their rations?

    a. 22

    b. 7

    c. 35

    d. 18

19. Who killed the first American serviceman during World War II?

    a. The Germans

    b. The Japanese

    c. The Russians

    d. The Americans

20. In what year did Japan surrender, officially ending World War II in Asia?

a. 1946
b. 1945
c. 1949
d. 1947

ANSWER KEY

1. C- 1917

2. A- President Woodrow Wilson

3. A- True

4. B- The Selective Service Act of 1917

5. A- Yes

6. A- True

7. D- 22,000

8. B- Treaty of Versailles

9. A- December 7, 1941

10. B- Hiroshima and Nagasaki

11. A- True

12. D- 350,000

13. B- Rosie the Riveter

14. A- 120,000

15. C- 291,557

16. A- Calvin Leon Graham, age 12

17. A- True

18. A- 22

19. C- The Russians

20. B- 1945

DID YOU KNOW?

1. Female suffrage advocates linked the patriotic efforts of women in World War I and the United States' struggle for democracy abroad to highlight the battle being ignored at home: advocacy for women's right to vote. The strategy was highly effective and shortly after World War I ended, women were granted the right to vote with the passage of the 19th Amendment.

2. Over 400,000 United States soldiers contracted STDs during World War I. Why? The United States was the only allied power in the war that did not provide condoms for their soldiers. This was because the Comstock Act did not allow any type of birth control devices or educational information to be shipped abroad to the soldiers.

3. The United States entered World War I so late in the game that the country only spent about seven and a half months in combat before the war ended.

4. World War I had numerous names including The Great War, The War of the Nations, The War to End All Wars, and the First World War.

5. During World War II, so many items were in such short supply that war ration books were issued to American families dictating how much food and other sought-after items they were allowed to have. Some of the items that

were rationed included gas, sugar, meat, shoes, and nylon stockings.

6. Before the locals in Hawaii knew that the Japanese had just attacked them, they welcomed Japanese pilot, Shigenori Nishikaichi, who had crash-landed in Hawaii. They made him breakfast and threw him a luau. The pilot participated in the luau by picking up a guitar and playing a traditional Japanese song for the locals.

7. There were wartime versions of American cookbooks released during World War II that gave suggestions on how to revise recipes to substitute for unavailable items.

8. During World War II, in the United States and other countries across the world, gardens were planted to grow vegetables, fruits, and herbs. Some of the most popular produce grown included beans, carrots, kale, peas, tomatoes, and cabbage. These "Victory Gardens" reduced the pressure of the limited food supply available around the world.

9. Many United States industries were forced to switch focus to keep up with the war effort. Auto factories had to stop making new cars and start making military vehicles instead. Whiskey distilleries had to repurpose themselves to produce industrial alcohol needed to make torpedo fuel.

10. The rate of cigarette smoking tripled in the United States during World War II. Free cigarettes were given out to the troops and they were also included in ration kits.

CHAPTER 7

THE CIVIL RIGHTS
MOVEMENT QUIZ

1. What were the Jim Crow Laws?

   a. Laws that made slavery legal

   b. Laws at the state and local level that enforced racial segregation in the South

   c. Federal laws that made it illegal for African Americans to ride the same buses as white Americans

   d. Federal laws that forbid African American women from voting

2. In what year was the 15th Amendment passed, granting Black men the right to vote?

   a. 1920

   b. 1870

   c. 1965

   d. 1940

3. What is the name of the landmark Supreme Court Case in 1954 that ruled that racial segregation in public schools was unconstitutional?

a. Plessy v. Ferguson

b. Brown v. Board of Education of Topeka

c. Angela v. U.S. Government

d. John v. Smith

4. Who was the 14-year-old African American boy who was brutally murdered in Mississippi in 1955 for allegedly flirting with a white woman?

a. Emmett Till

b. Bobby Seal

c. Fred Hampton

a. Roy Bryant

5. How old was Martin Luther King, Jr. when he was assassinated?

a. 50

b. 30

c. 65

d. 39

6. What famous musician performed at the March on Washington?

a. Elvis Presley

b. Bob Dylan

c. The Backstreet Boys

d. Aretha Franklin

7. Who founded the Black Panther Party in the 1960s?

a. Bobby Seale and Huey Newton

b. Martin Luther King, Jr.

c. Malcolm X

d. JFK

8. What was the Freedom Summer, also known as "the Mississippi Summer Project"?

a. A sit-in at lunch counters across the country

b. A voter registration drive in Mississippi

c. A summer of free love and music to boost spirits

d. An anti-war protest

9. What famous woman refused to give up her seat on the bus to a white person in Montgomery, Alabama and sparked the year-long Montgomery Bus Boycott?

a. Ella Baker

b. Harper Lee

c. Rosa Parks

d. Zora Neale Hurston

10. Who was the first Black student to enroll at the University of Mississippi?

a. James Meredith

b. Martin Luther King, Jr.

c. John Smith

d. Malcolm X

11. With what team did Jackie Robinson sign in 1946, becoming the first African American to play in Major League Baseball (MLB)?

a. Yankees

b. Brooklyn Dodgers

c. Phillies

d. Mets

12. Martin Luther King Jr.'s name given at birth was Michael, not Martin.

   a. True
   b. False

13. How many books did Martin Luther King Jr. write?

   a. None
   b. 2
   c. 5
   d. 7

14. Who was the leader of the Student Non-Violent Coordinating Committee (SNCC), who popularized the term "Black Power"?

   a. Martin Luther King
   b. Stokely Carmichael
   c. Malcolm X
   d. Maya Angelou

15. In what year was the Civil Rights Act passed, officially ending segregation in public places and in employment?

   a. 1950
   b. 1960
   c. 1964
   d. 1972

16. What became known as "Bloody Sunday"?

a. The day that Martin Luther King, Jr. was killed

b. The day that students were killed for registering voters in Mississippi

c. The day that Emmett Till was brutally murdered

d. The day that hundreds of civil rights marchers were attacked on the Edmund Pettus Bridge during their march out of Selma

17. What was the name of the brave woman who served as Martin Luther King's "right-hand woman" and secretary from 1955–1960, despite numerous threats against her and her family's lives?

a. Maude Ballou

b. Diane Nash

c. Natalie Smith

d. Ella Fitzgerald

18. Which Civil Rights activist, who participated in the Selma to Montgomery marches and was the youngest speaker at the March on Washington, is still fighting and led a sit-in in the House of Representatives for gun control in 2016?

a. Elizabeth Warren

b. Ta-Nehisi Coates

c. Roy Wilkins

d. John Lewis

19. What does the NAACP stand for?

a. National Association for the Advancement of Colored People

b. National Association for the Advancement of Civil Protections

c. National Association for the Argument of Civil Privileges

d. National Association for the Amelioration of Civilian Preservation

20. After the Civil Rights Movement, all people in the United States were treated equally.

a. True

b. False

ANSWER KEY

1. B- Laws at the state and local level that enforced racial segregation in the South

2. B- 1870

3. B- Brown v. Board of Education of Topeka

4. A- Emmett Till

5. D- 39

6. B- Bob Dylan

7. A- Bobby Seale and Huey Newton

8. B- A voter registration drive in Mississippi

9. C- Rosa Parks

10. A- James Meredith

11. B- Brooklyn Dodgers

12. A- True

13. C- 5

14. B- Stokely Carmichael

15. C- 1964

16. D- The day that hundreds of civil rights marchers were attacked on the Edmund Pettus Bridge during their march out of Selma

17. A- Maude Ballou

18. D- John Lewis

19. A- National Association for the Advancement of Colored People

20. B- False, discrimination against anyone who is not a white male is still something the United States is grappling with today

DID YOU KNOW?

1. In 1957, nine students—known as the "Little Rock Nine"—were escorted into Central High School under armed guard after President Eisenhower had to deploy federal troops to force the Governor of Arkansas to comply with the verdict of *Board v. Board of Education of Topeka.*

2. In 1961, a group of white and African American activists took bus trips called "the Freedom Rides" across the south to protest segregated bus terminals. They would conduct non-violent actions such as using "whites-only" bathrooms and lunch counters in the bus stations. They faced terrible violence from protestors but continued their journey. The Freedom Riders brought awareness across the world to the American Civil Rights Movement.

3. Rosa Parks was not the first activist to refuse to give up her seat on the bus. Claudette Colvin, a 15-year-old civil rights activist, was removed from a bus and jailed after she refused to give up her seat to a white person, nine months before Rosa Parks. She was a teenager and became pregnant after her arrest, so many viewed her to be the wrong person to be the face of the movement.

4. In 1960, four African American students from North Carolina A&T State University staged a sit-in at Woolworth's in Greensboro, which was infamous for

refusing to serve African Americans at their lunch counter. The group of men, known as the Greensboro Four, sparked sit-ins across the south. The lunch counter is now on display in Washington, D.C. at the National Museum of American History.

5. Martin Luther King Jr. was killed on Maya Angelou's birthday. For years after his death, Maya Angelou did not celebrate her birthday. She would meet, call, or send flowers to Coretta Scott King, Martin Luther King Jr.'s widow, every year on April 4th.

6. Martin Luther King Jr. was imprisoned a total of 29 times. Despite the circumstances of his arrests, he was always non-violent and encouraged others to practice non-violence.

7. Georgia Gilmore, a cook and activist, fed the civil rights movement, both literally and financially. She organized women to sell food like pound cakes and fried fish at churches, beauty salons, and at meetings to raise money to pay for the transportation system in Montgomery during the bus boycott.

8. As impressive as the March on Washington for Jobs and Freedom in 1963 was, the sexism that was present in the Civil Rights Movement was evident on this monumental day. Only one woman, Daisy Bates, was given the opportunity to speak at the March on Washington and she was given extraordinarily little time. Additionally, women were directed to march separately and had to

march behind the men. Coretta Scott King, Martin Luther King Jr.'s wife, expressed her disappointment in not being able to march next to her husband.

9. The 1964 Civil Rights Act had the longest filibuster in the history of the United States Senate. Despite the filibuster, the Civil Rights Act was still passed a little less than a year after the assassination of President John F. Kennedy.

10. Coretta Scott King was an extremely intelligent woman and was the Valedictorian of her high school class. She wrote a book that was published in 1969 titled *My Life with Martin Luther King, Jr.* After her husband's assassination, she went on to found the Martin Luther King Jr. Center for Nonviolent Social Change.

CHAPTER 8

WOMEN'S HISTORY QUIZ

1. Who was the abolitionist who wrote *Uncle Tom's Cabin,* a novel published in 1852 that had a deep effect on the way slavery was viewed in the United States?

    a. Harriet Beecher Stowe
    b. Harriet Tubman
    c. Mary Wollstonecraft
    d. Jane Austen

2. Who was the first woman to be nominated for President of the United States in 1872?

    a. Susan B. Anthony
    b. Victoria Woodhull
    c. Sojourner Truth
    d. Hillary Clinton

3. Who founded the National Woman Suffrage Association?

    a. Elizabeth Cady Stanton and Susan B. Anthony
    b. Alice Paul
    c. Lucretia Mott and Carrie Chapman Catt
    d. Mary Todd Lincoln

4. The Equal Rights Amendment was first drafted in 1923 by which famous suffragist?

    a. Carrie Chapman Catt
    b. Alice Paul
    c. Eleanor Roosevelt
    d. Elizabeth Cady Stanton

5. Who was the first woman to serve as a Supreme Court Justice of the United States?

    a. Ruth Bader Ginsburg
    b. Sonia Sotomayor
    c. Sandra Day O'Connor
    d. Hillary Clinton

6. Sojourner Truth, who delivered the famous speech, "Ain't I a woman?" at the Women's Rights Convention in Ohio in 1851, was a former slave.

    a. True
    b. False

7. Who led hundreds of slaves to freedom in the north as a conductor on the Underground Railroad?

    a. Sojourner Truth
    b. Frederica Douglas
    c. Harriet Tubman
    d. Susan B. Anthony

8. Women who were arrested for picketing the White House for women's suffrage were imprisoned, beaten, and force-fed.

a. True

b. False

9. The United States finally passed the Equal Rights Amendment in the 1970s.

a. True

b. False

10. Which landmark case in 1973 ruled that the Constitution protects a woman's right to choose to have an abortion without excessive government restriction?

a. Brown v. Board of Education

b. Roe v. Wade

c. Plessy v. Ferguson

d. Loving v. Virginia

11. The 19th Amendment, which granted women the right to vote, is also known as the...

a. Alice Paul Amendment

b. Susan B. Anthony Amendment

c. Elizabeth Cady Stanton Amendment

d. About Time Amendment

12. Who was the first woman elected to the United States Senate?

a. Hattie Wyatt Caraway

b. Elizabeth Cady Stanton

c. Eleanor Roosevelt

d. Sojourner Truth

13. Frances Perkins, the first female cabinet member, served as the Secretary of Labor and played a key role in drafting what important piece of legislation?

    a. The Emancipation Proclamation
    b. The Civil Rights Act
    c. The Equal Rights Amendment
    d. The New Deal

14. The Equal Pay Act of 1963, signed into law by John F. Kennedy, revised the Fair Labor Standards Act and aimed to eliminate wage disparities based on sex. This law has been extremely effective in eliminating the gender pay gap in the United States.

    a. True
    b. False

15. Who was the first woman to be nominated for president by a major political party in the United States?

    a. Susan B. Anthony
    b. Belva Lockwood
    c. Charlene Mitchell
    d. Hillary Clinton

16. The day after President Donald Trump's inauguration, the Women's March, a worldwide protest, was held and women wore what item?

    a. Pink t-shirts
    b. Pink pussyhats
    c. Pink bandanas
    d. Pink jackets

17. Who is the author of the famous book, *The Feminine Mystique,* which was one of the catalysts of the second-wave feminist movement?

    a. Gloria Steinem

    b. Virginia Woolf

    c. Maya Angelou

    d. Betty Friedan

18. Title IX is a federal civil rights law that protects _____.

    a. People from being discriminated against based on sex in the hiring process.

    b. People from being discriminated against based on sex in education programs or activities that receive federal funding, like public schools.

    c. People from being discriminated against based on their sexual orientation.

    d. People from being discriminated against based on whether they are pro-life or pro-choice.

19. Supreme Court Justice Ruth Bader Ginsburg, also known as "The Notorious R.B.G.," was the first supreme court justice to _____?

    a. Dissent on every case relating to women

    b. Preside over a same-sex wedding

    c. Visit Russia on behalf of the United States

    d. Support women's reproductive rights

20. Who became the first woman in the history of the United States to become the Speaker of the House?

a. Elizabeth Warren

b. Hillary Clinton

c. Nancy Pelosi

d. Lisa Murkowski

ANSWER KEY

1. A- Harriet Beecher Stowe

2. B- Victoria Woodhull

3. A- Elizabeth Cady Stanton and Susan B. Anthony

4. B- Alice Paul

5. C- Sandra Day O'Connor

6. A- True

7. C- Harriet Tubman

8. A- True

9. B- False, to date the United States has still not passed the Equal Rights Amendment

10. B- Roe v. Wade

11. B- Susan B. Anthony Amendment

12. A- Hattie Wyatt Caraway

13. D- The New Deal

14. B- False, as of 2019, women make $0.79 for every dollar that men make

15. D- Hillary Clinton

16. B- Pink pussyhats

17. D- Betty Friedan

18. B- People from being discriminated against based on sex

in education programs or activities that receive federal funding, like public schools.

19. B- Preside over a same-sex wedding

20. C- Nancy Pelosi

DID YOU KNOW?

1. After being banned from attending the World Anti-Slavery Convention, Lucretia Mott and Elizabeth Cady Stanton decided to hold a women's rights convention in Seneca Falls, New York in 1848. At this convention, Elizabeth Cady Stanton presented her *Declaration of Sentiments.*

2. In 1916, Alice Paul, a Quaker, founded the National Woman's Party (NWP), a more militant branch of a women's suffrage organization. The women went on to picket the White House, get arrested, and push the issue of women's suffrage to the forefront of the American political consciousness.

3. The women's suffrage campaign colors were purple, white, and gold.

4. Elouise P. Cobell has a laundry list of accomplishments, and many people have never even heard of her. Also known as "Yellow Bird Woman," she was a Native American woman who confronted the United States government in the largest class-action suit against the government in history. In this landmark case, *Cobell v. Salazar*, she challenged the government for the mismanagement of over 500,000 Native Americans' trust funds. One of the outcomes of this case is a $60 million scholarship that is provided for Native Americans and Alaskan Natives. Cobell also helped found the Blackfeet

National Bank, the first Native American bank, and served as the Executive Director of the Native American Community Development Corporation.

5. The First Lady Eleanor Roosevelt held press conferences at the White House for women only. She held the first press conference for women reporters in March 1933 and subsequently held 348 more during her time at the White House. This was particularly unique at the time given the fact that the media strongly discriminated against women in the field.

6. Women in the United States were not allowed to have credit cards in their name until 1974 when the Equal Credit Opportunity Act was passed.

7. Madeleine Albright became the first woman to become Secretary of State in 1997 and was the first Secretary of State in U.S. history to travel to North Korea.

8. On July 1, 2000, Vermont became the first state in the United States to legalize same-sex marriage. The first couple to get married, inspiring many in the LGBT movement, were Carolyn Conrad and Kathleen Peterson.

9. Hillary Clinton's fashion has been talked about positively and negatively by many. In the statement, "If I want to knock a story off the front page, I just change my hairstyle," Clinton reminded us all that female politicians in the United States and around the world are treated differently than men.

10. First Lady Michelle Obama was an accomplished woman. After she graduated from Princeton University, she went on to law school at Harvard. While studying at Harvard, she advocated for others, participating in demonstrations demanding that Harvard accept more students and professors of color.

CHAPTER 9

FROM BLUES TO ROCK
AND ROLL QUIZ

1. Jazz was born in this U.S. city:

    a. New York City

    b. New Orleans

    c. Chicago

    d. Miami

2. The first blues music ever heard was on the streets of Mississippi.

    a. True

    b. False

3. In 1920, which woman became the first African American singer to record a blues song that went on to sell one million copies in a year?

    a. Ella Fitzgerald

    b. Ma Rainey

    c. Mamie Smith

    d. Maya Angelou

4. Who is known as the "Empress of the Blues"?

   a. Bessie Smith
   b. Charley Patton
   c. Ella Fitzgerald
   d. Taylor Swift

5. Country music was originally called "Hillbilly Music."

   a. True
   b. False

6. Who was the first country music artist to become famous?

   a. Johnny Cash
   b. The Carter Family
   c. Taylor Swift
   d. Jenny Lou Carson

7. What famous American rock band formed in Los Angeles in 1965 and sang the song "People Are Strange"?

   a. The Beatles
   b. The Doors
   c. Simon and Garfunkel
   d. Led Zeppelin

8. What was country music singer Johnny Cash's first number one song?

   a. "A Boy Named Sue"
   b. "Ballad of a Teenage Queen"
   c. "I Walk the Line"
   d. "God's Country"

9. Where did famous singer-songwriter Taylor Swift grow up?

    a. In the NYC suburbs

    b. On a ranch in the Midwest

    c. Nashville

    d. On a Christmas tree farm in Pennsylvania

10. How many Grammys did Elvis Presley, the King of Rock and Roll, win?

    a. None

    b. 3

    c. 10

    d. 5

11. Who was the lead singer and guitarist of The Grateful Dead?

    a. Paul McCartney

    b. Jerry Garcia

    c. Richard Wright

    d. Jim Morrison

12. In what town did the infamous Woodstock Music Festival in 1969 take place?

    a. Woodstock, New York

    b. New Paltz, New York

    c. Zena, New York

    d. Bethel, New York

13. Who did NOT perform at the Woodstock Music Festival?

    a. Jimi Hendrix

b. Led Zeppelin

c. The Who

d. Joan Baez

14. Where was Michael Jackson born?

   a. California

   b. New York

   c. Indiana

   d. Georgia

15. When did the underground urban movement of hip-hop begin?

   a. The mid-1970s

   b. 1981

   c. 1967

   d. 1987

16. Where in the United States did hip-hop originate?

   a. Southside, Chicago

   b. New Orleans

   c. Los Angeles

   d. The Bronx, New York

17. Which famous rapper's real name is Calvin Broadus?

   a. Jay-Z

   b. Eminem

   c. Snoop Dog

   d. Tupac

18. What is the best-selling single in world history?

a. Bing Crosby's "White Christmas"

b. The Beatles "Hey Jude"

c. Taylor Swift "Love Story"

d. Ed Sheeran "Shape of You"

19. What song is considered by many to be the catchiest song of all time?

a. Backstreet Boys "Everybody"

b. Spice Girls "Wannabe"

c. Maroon 5 "Memories"

d. Robin Thicke "Blurred Lines"

20. What was Miley Cyrus' birth name?

a. Sunshine Ray

b. Miley Cyrus

c. Feather Ray

d. Destiny Hope

ANSWER KEY

1. B- New Orleans

2. A- True

3. C- Mamie Smith

4. A- Bessie Smith

5. A- True

6. B- The Carter Family

7. B- The Doors

8. C- "I Walk the Line"

9. D- On a Christmas tree farm in Pennsylvania

10. C- 10

11. B- Jerry Garcia

12. D- Bethel, New York

13. B- Led Zeppelin

14. C- Indiana

15. A- The mid-1970s

16. D- The Bronx, New York

17. C- Snoop Dog

18. A- Bing Crosby's "White Christmas"

19. B- Spice Girls "Wannabe"

20. D- Destiny Hope

DID YOU KNOW?

1. Musicians who played early blues street music played not only instruments but regular household items as well. Musicians could be found playing guitars, banjos, and harmonicas—plus washboards and spoons.

2. Tin Pan Alley was an actual location in Manhattan on West 28th Street between 5th and 6th Avenue where music publishers had their businesses. Tin Pan Alley music is also the name of a genre of popular early 20th-century music in the United States.

3. Jazz musician Louis Armstrong began playing in brass-band parades in New Orleans at age 13. He was one of the most influential jazz musicians in history.

4. Ella Fitzgerald and Marilyn Monroe had a strong friendship that was ahead of their time, as racial prejudice was still quite overt. Despite her obvious talent, Fitzgerald had a hard time getting booked at any large jazz clubs, primarily because she was a heavy-set woman. The owner of a large club in LA thought Ella Fitzgerald was not "glamorous enough" to draw in the crowds. Marilyn Monroe intervened, advocating for Fitzgerald by saying that she would be in the front row every night and would fill the seats with other stars. Monroe was true to her word, but it was not necessary. Fitzgerald's shows sold out and she never had to play another small jazz club again.

5. Prince, considered one of the most original artists in popular American music history, wrote his first song titled "Funk Machine" at age seven and signed a contract with Warner Brothers at the young age of 19.

6. Bruce Springsteen's "Born in the USA" was the first CD made in the United States in 1984.

7. In 2015, singer Taylor Swift earned $1 million per day.

8. Prince, one of the most influential American musicians in the 1980s, was a fervent Jehovah's Witness. He was baptized in 2001 and even went door-to-door to spread the word of his faith.

9. Beloved music celebrity Beyoncé began singing as a soloist in her church choir at the young age of seven. Her full name is Beyoncé Giselle Knowles-Carter.

10. As if Madonna has not accomplished enough with her successful music career, she is also an author. She has authored 12 coffee table books, seven picture books for children, and 12 children's chapter books. Her first children's book, *The English Roses*, was on The New York Times Best Seller list.

CHAPTER 10

HOLLYWOOD—MOVIES, TV, AND CELEBRITIES QUIZ

1. The world's first sync-sound musical film was produced in the United States in 1927. What is the name of this famous film?

    a. *Gone with the Wind*

    b. *The Jazz Singer*

    c. *Casablanca*

    d. *Mary Poppins*

2. Marilyn Monroe was put into foster care when she was just two weeks old and her mother was diagnosed as schizophrenic.

    a. True

    b. False

3. Who starred in the 1939 musical film, *The Wizard of Oz?*

    a. Marilyn Monroe

    b. Shirley Temple

    c. Margaret Smith

    d. Judy Garland

4. In the original draft of the epic movie series *Star Wars*, the beloved R2-D2:

   a. Spoke English instead of "robot talk"
   b. Was a monkey
   c. Was obsessed with jellybeans
   d. Was a donkey

5. Who starred in the iconic film *Forrest Gump*?

   a. Robin Williams
   b. Tom Hanks
   c. Will Smith
   d. Kevin Spacey

6. *Titanic*, released in 1997, was nominated for 14 Academy Awards, won 11 Oscars, and included what hit single that became number one across the globe after the film's release?

   a. "I'll Never Let Go"
   b. "Pretty Woman"
   c. "My Heart Will Go On"
   d. "Heartbreaker"

7. Which American film does the quote, "I'm gonna make him an offer he can't refuse," come from?

   a. *American Gangster*
   b. *The Godfather*
   c. *Rambo*
   d. *Goodfellas*

8. What is the name of the main character in *Home Alone,* starring Macaulay Culkin?

a. Kevin Jones

b. Buzz McCallister

c. Harry Lime

d. Kevin McCallister

9. What was the first Disney movie ever made?

   a. *Fantasia*

   b. *Pinocchio*

   c. *Cinderella*

   d. *Snow White and the Seven Dwarfs*

10. What is the most-watched television broadcast in the United States?

    a. The Oscars

    b. The Bachelor

    c. The Super Bowl

    d. The Grammys

11. After her acting career, Grace Kelly became what?

    a. A supermodel

    b. A princess

    c. A cowgirl

    d. A poet

12. Who was the first-ever host of Saturday Night Live?

    a. George Carlin

    b. Tom Hanks

    c. Candace Bergen

    d. Harry Styles

13. What year did the children's show *Sesame Street* first air on PBS?

    a. 1981
    b. 1975
    c. 1971
    d. 1969

14. Who played the part of Samantha in the classic TV show *Bewitched*?

    a. Audrey Hepburn
    b. Elizabeth Montgomery
    c. Mia Farrow
    d. Tina Louise

15. Where do Homer, Marge, Bart, and Lisa live in the television show *The Simpsons*?

    a. Springfield
    b. Chicago
    c. Springtown
    d. Portland

16. Where did the code in *The Matrix* come from?

    a. *The Great Gatsby* novel translated into Japanese
    b. Japanese sushi recipes
    c. Pop lyrics from the Backstreet Boys in Japanese
    d. Random Japanese restaurant menus

17. Sean Connery wore a toupee in every *James Bond* movie because he started going bald at the young age of 17.

    a. True
    b. False

18. In 1982, Steven Spielberg worked on two movies that parallel each other in many ways, *E.T. the Extra-Terrestrial* and _____.

    a. *Jaws*
    b. *Raiders of the Lost Ark*
    c. *Jurassic Park*
    d. *Poltergeist*

19. What was the first Disney movie produced after the death of Walt Disney?

    a. *The Little Mermaid*
    b. *The Aristocats*
    c. *Cinderella*
    d. *The Lion King*

20. Which movie did Denzel Washington NOT star in?

    a. *American Gangster*
    b. *Malcolm X*
    c. *The Pursuit of Happyness*
    d. *Crimson Tide*

ANSWER KEY

1. B- *The Jazz Singer*

2. A- True

3. D- Judy Garland

4. A- Spoke English instead of "robot talk"

5. B- Tom Hanks

6. C- "My Heart Will Go On"

7. B- *The Godfather*

8. D- Kevin McCallister

9. D- *Snow White and the Seven Dwarfs*

10. C- The Super Bowl

11. B- A princess

12. A- George Carlin

13. D- 1969

14. B-Elizabeth Montgomery

15. A- Springfield

16. B- Japanese sushi recipes

17. A- True

18. D- *Poltergeist*

19. B- *The Aristocats*

20. C- *The Pursuit of Happyness*

DID YOU KNOW?

1. The only star on the Hollywood Walk of Fame that is not on the sidewalk is Muhammad Ali's. He "did not want to be walked on," so his star was placed on the wall of the Kodak Theater instead.

2. *Game of Thrones* was broadcast in 207 countries and territories around the world. The show was filmed in ten countries and had 50 filming locations in Ireland alone.

3. The classic horror film *The Shining*, based on the novel written by Stephen King, was inspired by a real hotel in Colorado, the Stanley Hotel. King and his wife, Tabitha, visited The Stanley and stayed in room 217; they were the only guests in the hotel at the time. The Stanley is included in many lists of the most haunted places in the United States. Hotel staff report hearing people having a party in the kitchen when it is empty, as well as piano music playing in the ballroom when no one is there. The Stanley Hotel is still open, and they have a dedicated in-house TV channel that plays *The Shining* 24 hours a day.

4. Tim Burton, the American director and producer, was a talented artist long before he was ever a director or producer. He was an avid drawer from a young age, and he developed his unique style early on. Some of Burton's most loved characters, including Edward Scissorhands and Jack Skellington from *The Nightmare Before Christmas*, came from his illustrations in his youth.

5. Before *The Fast and the Furious* was filmed, Michelle Rodriguez and Jordana Brewster did not even have driver's licenses.

6. George Lucas, the creator of *Star Wars*, purchased a fire truck and paid a staff of 14 firefighters. His team is called the Skywalker Fire Department and has been around for about 30 years. They have an agreement with the county they are located in to assist with fires when needed and have helped put out numerous wildfires in Marin County, California.

7. American actor Christopher Walken worked as a professional dancer and a circus lion tamer before becoming an actor.

8. In America you can insure anything, even body parts. Actress Julia Roberts insured her smile for 30 million dollars.

9. Before the filming of the popular TV show *The Walking Dead*, English actor Andrew Lincoln practiced his Southern accent by going out and ordering coffee and fried chicken.

10. American actress and filmmaker Angelina Jolie is the highest-paid actress in Hollywood.

CHAPTER 11

LANDSCAPES AND LANDMARKS QUIZ

1. The Declaration of Independence was signed in 1776 in Independence Hall in which United States City?

    a. New York City
    b. Boston
    c. Richmond
    d. Philadelphia

2. Which United States president cannot be found on Mt. Rushmore, the famous United States landmark in South Dakota?

    a. John Quincy Adams
    b. George Washington
    c. Abraham Lincoln
    d. Theodore Roosevelt

3. Which multi-storied, adobe, Native American community—considered to be the oldest continuously inhabited community in the U.S.—has been inhabited for over 1,000 years?

a. Mesa Verde

b. Taos Pueblo

c. Tijuana

d. Shongopovi

4. The Statue of Liberty is not actually located in New York City.

   a. True

   b. False

5. Philadelphia, Pennsylvania was the first capital of the United States.

   a. True

   b. False

6. What was the first university in the United States?

   a. Yale

   b. Harvard

   c. Princeton

   d. Stanford

7. Glacier National Park, considered one of the most beautiful national parks in the United States with more than 700 lakes and parts of two mountain ranges, can be found in which state?

   a. Washington

   b. Montana

   c. Oregon

   d. Idaho

8. The 49th state, Alaska, is home to the tallest mountain in North America. What is the name of the peak?

    a. Mount Kilimanjaro

    b. Mount Everest

    c. Denali

    d. Delaney

9. What is the name of the oldest national park, which was founded in 1872?

    a. Yellowstone

    b. Yosemite

    c. Joshua Tree

    d. Acadia

10. There is an island inhabited by monkeys in the state of South Carolina that is not accessible to humans.

    a. True

    b. False

11. What is the name of the island in the United States that has been home to wild ponies for hundreds of years?

    a. Edisto Island

    b. Pony Island

    c. Mount Desert Island

    d. Assateague Island

12. There are over 2,500 National Historic Landmarks in the United States and two of them can move. What are these two monuments?

    a. Hoover Dam and the Statue of Liberty

b. San Francisco cable cars and New Orleans' St. Charles streetcar

c. U.S.S. Chesapeake Warship and the NYC streetcar

d. U.S.S. California and the San Francisco trolley

13. The United States Library of Congress in Washington, D.C., is the largest in the world and has more than 170 million items.

a. True

b. False

14. The state of Kentucky is home to the world's longest cave system, with more than 400 miles of mapped passageways. What is the name of this cave system?

a. Bat Cave

b. Carlsbad Caverns

c. Wind Cave

d. Mammoth Cave

15. Bison, the largest mammal in North America, almost became extinct but today they are thriving. In what national park in the United States can they be found?

a. Acadia National Park

b. Yosemite National Park

c. Glacier National Park

d. Yellowstone National Park

16. Grizzly bears can no longer be found in the United States.

a. True

b. False

17. The tallest tree species in the world can grow more than 350 feet tall and 24 feet wide and can only be found from central California to southern Oregon. What is the name of the species?

    a. Cypress
    b. Coast Redwood
    c. Giant Sequoia
    d. Eucalyptus

18. What is the name of the estate of America's third president, which can be visited today in Charlottesville, Virginia?

    a. Hyde Park
    b. Mount Vernon
    c. Peacefield
    d. Monticello

19. An estimated 40% of United States citizens can trace one of their ancestors back to this famous island which used to be an immigration inspection station?

    a. Ellis Island
    b. Easter Island
    c. Assateague Island
    d. Liberty Island

20. What are the names of the Great Lakes, one of the world's largest freshwater ecosystems?

    a. Superior, Michigan, Huron, Erie, and Ontario
    b. Chicago, Michigan, Erie, Milwaukee, and Ontario
    c. Superior, Chicago, Erie, Ontario, and Pennsylvania
    d. Chicago, Erie, Ontario, Montana, and Huron

ANSWER KEY

1. D- Philadelphia

2. A- John Quincy Adams

3. B- Taos Pueblo

4. A- True

5. A- True

6. B- Harvard

7. B- Montana

8. C- Denali

9. A- Yellowstone

10. A- True

11. D- Assateague Island

12. B- San Francisco cable cars and New Orleans' St. Charles streetcar

13. A- True

14. D- Mammoth Cave

15. D- Yellowstone National Park

16. B- False

17. B- Coast Redwood

18. D- Monticello

19. A- Ellis Island

20. A- Superior, Michigan, Huron, Erie, and Ontario

DID YOU KNOW?

1. Two women, Florence Thorne and Margaret Scattergood, purchased land and a home in the Virginia woods in 1933. The federal government wanted to buy the property and the women agreed to sell 30 acres of their land, provided they would be able to live there until they died. The government agreed to the deal and the women ended up living on the grounds of the Central Intelligence Agency for 40 years.

2. In Alaska you can get a great view of the Northern Lights, also known as the aurora borealis, which are bright streaks of colored light that shine across the night sky.

3. White Sands National Monument, located in the Chihuahuan Desert in the state of New Mexico, is a landmark that is often overlooked but should not be. It is home to majestic white gypsum dunes that look like snow. These 275 square miles of desert comprise the world's largest gypsum dune field. It is also a photographer's dream.

4. In the state of Michigan, there is a labyrinth of French lavender so large that it takes you an hour to walk to the center. You can even see it from space!

5. There is a town in Washington state, Longview, which has built treetop bridges designed to help squirrels cross the street.

6. The beautiful, multi-colored Grand Prismatic Spring, located in Yellowstone National Park, is the third-largest hot spring in the world and the largest hot spring in the United States. It is one of the most popular places to visit in Yellowstone National Park.

7. Biscayne National Park in Florida is one of the United States' best-kept secrets. The national park has four marine ecosystems, including a mangrove forest, the Bay, the Keys, and coral reefs. It is also home to numerous threatened species of animals like the American crocodile, sea turtles, peregrine falcons, and the West Indian Manatee.

8. The elephant seal is a unique animal that can be found on Point Reyes National Seashore in the state of California. It really is an "elephant" of the sea. The elephant seal can be up to 20 feet long and weigh 8,800 pounds.

9. Petrified Forest National Park, located in Arizona, is a bizarre landscape filled with fossils that are primarily the remains of trees that have turned into hard quartz over millions of years.

10. There are miles of underground tunnels in Washington, D.C. They are used by senators and members of the House of Representatives to get around, and the public will never get to see most of them.

CHAPTER 12

CUSTOMS AND
TRADITIONS QUIZ

1. This holiday is celebrated every year in the United States on the 4th of July.

    a. Bastille Day
    b. Independence Day
    c. America is Awesome Day
    d. National Pride Day

2. The United States is often described as a _____, meaning its culture has been influenced by many different people from many different places.

    a. Culture pot
    b. Cookie
    c. Melting pot
    d. Rainbow

3. Women in the United States who are expecting their first child are treated to a party where friends and family bring gifts for the baby, eat food, and play games related to motherhood. What are these celebrations called?

a. Baby Party

b. Baby Showers

c. Welcome to Motherhood Party

d. Sprinkles

4. On the day after Thanksgiving, Americans brave crowds and crazy hours to get started on their holiday shopping with the best deals. What is this day called?

a. Deal Day

b. Elf on the Shelf

c. Black Friday

d. Cyber Tuesday

5. Every 4th of July, there is a marshmallow fight in Ocean Beach, California. The marshmallow fights got so out of control that the town tried to put a stop to the decades-long tradition and stationed police on all the local beaches.

a. True

b. False

6. What is Super Tuesday in the United States?

a. Primary election day, when the largest number of U.S. states hold primary elections and caucuses, during which roughly one-third of all delegates can be won

b. The day after Black Friday when everyone shops for holiday gifts online

c. Election day every four years, when the country elects the next president

d. The day when all fast food is supersized for the same price

7. Where is the annual Kentucky Derby horse race held every first Saturday in May?

    a. Lexington, Kentucky
    b. Bowling Green, Kentucky
    c. Louisville, Kentucky
    d. Mammoth Cave, Kentucky

8. What is Bonnaroo?

    a. An annual jazz festival that takes place in New Orleans
    b. An annual film festival that takes place in Houston, Texas
    c. An annual cherry pit spitting festival that takes place in Maryland
    d. An annual four-day music festival that takes place in Tennessee

9. Every fall in Marlinton, West Virginia, there is a Roadkill Cook-off where everything is made from dead animals found on the side of the road, and you can taste items like biscuits in squirrel gravy.

    a. True
    b. False

10. What is the name of the annual 1000-mile sled dog race across Alaska every March?

    a. Race to Anchorage
    b. Iditarod Trail Sled Dog Race

    c. American Dog Derby

    d. Dog Winter Olympics

11. Which of the following items is NOT dropped on New Year's Eve in cities around the United States?

    a. A giant Peep chick

    b. A beach ball

    c. A conch shell

    d. A human-sized pepperoni pizza

12. The Friday before Martin Luther King Jr. Day, the state of Virginia celebrates the birthdays of two confederate generals, _____ and _____.

    a. Jefferson Davis and Robert E. Lee

    b. Braxton Bragg and George Pickett

    c. Ulysses S. Grant and Robert Anderson

    d. Robert E. Lee and Stonewall Jackson

13. Every August 16th, the state of Vermont observes a state holiday to celebrate Bennington Battle Day, which was a battle during the Revolutionary War that took place in New York.

    a. True

    b. False

14. What is punkin chunkin?

    a. A pumpkin pie eating contest that occurs in the fall in the United States

    b. The act of chucking pumpkins using devices such as slingshots, catapults, and cannons

c. The act of cutting pumpkins to make jack-o-lanterns for Halloween

d. The act of smashing old pumpkins in the street after Halloween is over

15. How many pounds of chocolate is purchased in the United States in the week before Valentine's Day, the holiday of love?

   a. 18 million pounds
   b. 27 million pounds
   c. 43 million pounds
   d. 58 million pounds

16. On March 17th every year, the United States observes St. Patrick's Day. Which United States city dyes its river green to celebrate?

   a. New York City
   b. Chicago
   c. Los Angeles
   d. Charleston

17. Why does election day in the United States always fall on a Tuesday in early November?

   a. The United States' agrarian societies needed time to travel to voting locations and by early November the harvest was done

   b. United States citizens refused to give up their time drinking and participating in weekend festivities to make the time to vote and turnout was low

   c. Congress passed a law about when election day would be held without much thought as to when;

they just picked what was convenient for them at the time

    d. Roads were typically cleared on Mondays so horses and buggies could more easily travel on a Tuesday, especially from rural areas

18. In which United States city would you go to if you wanted Elvis to marry you?

    a. Austin, Texas

    b. Los Angeles, California

    c. Las Vegas, Nevada

    d. New York City, New York

19. Every year there is an Ostrich Festival during which people in Arizona race their ostriches.

    a. True

    b. False

20. Every Labor Day weekend in a small town in Maryland they race what creatures?

    a. Fish

    b. Snails

    c. Crabs

    d. Lobster

ANSWER KEY

1. B- Independence Day

2. C- Melting pot

3. B- Baby Showers

4. C- Black Friday

5. A- True

6. A- Primary election day, when the largest number of U.S. states hold primary elections and caucuses, during which roughly one-third of all delegates can be won

7. C- Louisville, Kentucky

8. D- An annual four-day music festival that takes place in Tennessee

9. A- True

10. B- Iditarod Trail Sled Dog Race

11. D- A human-sized pepperoni pizza

12. D- Robert E. Lee and Stonewall Jackson

13. B- False, the Battle of Bennington took place in New York

14. B- The act of chucking pumpkins using devices such as slingshots, catapults, and cannons

15. D- 58 million pounds

16. B- Chicago

17. A- The United States' agrarian societies needed time to

travel to voting locations and by early November the harvest was done

18. C- Las Vegas, Nevada

19. A- True

20. C- Crabs

DID YOU KNOW?

1. On the first Monday in September, the United States celebrates a holiday called 'Labor Day.' Labor Day celebrates the Labor Movement and American workers. It officially became a federal holiday in 1894. At the end of the 1800s, workers in the United States faced extremely harsh conditions: young children slaved away in factories, workers faced 12-hour days and seven-day weeks, and working conditions were extremely unsafe. In the face of strikes and riots, Congress passed this "workingmen's holiday" to attempt to "repair ties with American workers."

2. Every year on February 2nd, Americans celebrate something called "Groundhog Day." Americans wait anxiously to discover whether a groundhog will see his shadow. If he does not see his shadow, spring will come soon. If he does see his shadow, that means there will be six more weeks of winter. Despite the popularity of this tradition, there has been no scientific evidence to prove that this is an accurate way to predict spring weather.

3. Most people have heard of Thanksgiving, a day in which Americans give thanks and share a meal with loved ones. The holiday celebrates the early story of the Pilgrim's meal with Native Americans. But what most people have not heard about is the presidential turkey pardon. Every

year, the president saves a turkey from being eaten and sends one lucky turkey to live on a farm.

4. Hayes had a presidency full of "firsts," including the first White House Easter Egg Roll in 1878. He had reportedly been taking a walk when a group of children approached him, eager to be able to access the White House lawns to play egg-rolling games. President Hayes told the guards to let the children enter and it became an annual tradition on the White House lawn.

5. Every year in Nenana, Alaska, individuals guess the exact time that the Tanana River ice will break up. Known as the "Nenana Ice Classic," there is an annual ice pool and tickets go on sale from February 1st through April 2nd throughout Alaska. Although it used to be a betting pool, the Nenana Ice Classic is now a non-profit charitable gaming organization, so the proceeds of the pool benefit numerous volunteer and non-profit organizations.

6. The state of Kentucky is known for its bourbon, which has made its way into many traditions, even marriage. It is a tradition for a bride and groom to bury a bottle of bourbon at the site of their wedding to prevent rain on their wedding day. There are also particular rules to follow, including that the bourbon must be buried at least a month before the wedding and the bottle must be placed upside down. After the couple is married, they dig up the bottle and drink it with their wedding guests.

7. Ugly Christmas Sweater parties have become a fun part of

the holiday season in the United States. Hipsters and adults alike enjoy rocking Christmas sweaters decorated with snowmen, Santa, reindeer, Christmas lights, pom-poms, and jewels. The trick to pulling off the Ugly Christmas Sweater is the uglier the better, with the most popular sweaters being found at thrift stores, like the Salvation Army.

8. Richmond, Virginia has a time-honored tradition every holiday season of participating in something called "Tacky Light Tours." Groups take rides on trolleys, in limousines, or on buses to view houses with tacky holiday lights listed in the local newspaper, the *Richmond Times-Dispatch*. Only houses with at least 40,000 lights make the list and numerous houses have many more than that.

9. Burning Man is an annual event in Black Rock City, which is a temporary city set up in the desert of Nevada, specifically created for the Burning Man Festival. Taking place in late summer every year, the event is an experiment in community and art. One of the key components of Burning Man is gifting and decommodification; therefore, it is a "commerce-free" event and the only things that are sold are ice and coffee. Everything else is received or given as a gift.

10. SantaCon, which originated in San Francisco, is an annual pub crawl where people go from bar to bar dressed like Santa Claus. SantaCon has grown so large that it happens in cities around the world every holiday season.

CHAPTER 13

FOOD—THE DELICIOUS, THE UNHEALTHY, AND THE TRULY AMERICAN QUIZ

1. Which three foods, known as the "Three Sisters," largely made up the Native American diet and were staples for early settlers?

    a. Corn, potatoes, and broccoli

    b. Beans, corn, and squash

    c. Buffalo, bison, and deer

    d. Fish, beans, and corn

2. Indigenous people in northeastern North America were the first groups to produce this sweet treat that is extracted from trees.

    a. Candy

    b. Maple syrup

    c. Honey

    d. Root beer

3. New Orleans has food like no other city in the United States. Creole food was created in New Orleans and was

primarily influenced by the French, African, and Native American populations. What are some examples of signature Creole foods that you can find in New Orleans?

    a. Gumbo

    b. Jambalaya

    c. Calas

    d. All of the above

4. Po' Boys, a popular sandwich served on French bread with fillings like fried seafood (usually shrimp), were provided free of charge to feed which group of people in 1929?

    a. Garment workers whose wages were too low to feed their families

    b. Poor jazz musicians playing for tips on the streets of New Orleans

    c. Striking streetcar workers

    d. Military men stationed in New Orleans who did not have kitchens

5. Few Americans can fathom life without peanut butter and jelly sandwiches. Who patented the process of making peanut butter from raw peanuts in 1895?

    a. Thomas Jefferson

    b. Dr. John Harvey Kellogg

    c. Dr. John Butter

    d. Harvey Smith

6. Everyone knows how much Americans love pizza. In fact, they love it so much that they eat how many acres of pizza every day?

a. 50 acres

b. 70 acres

c. 90 acres

d. 100 acres

7. Which state is the number one dairy producer in the country?

a. Kansas

b. Virginia

c. California

d. New Jersey

8. Which U.S. city has earned the title "Ice Cream Capital of the World"?

a. New York City, New York

b. Le Mars, Iowa

c. Houston, Texas

d. Twin Falls, Idaho

9. Which state is known for its lobster?

a. New Hampshire

b. New Jersey

c. Florida

d. Maine

10. What type of pizza is famous in the U.S. city of Chicago?

a. Deep-dish

b. Pepperoni

c. Vegetable

d. Thin crust

11. The first McDonald's was opened in which city in 1937?

    a. San Francisco, California
    b. San Bernardino, California
    c. Orange County, California
    d. Yosemite, California

12. What do Americans like to eat for dessert when they go camping and make a fire?

    a. Reese's Peanut Butter Cups
    b. S'mores
    c. Ice Cream
    d. Oreos

13. It is no surprise that Americans consume a ton of food on Super Bowl Sunday. On average, how many chicken wings will be eaten on Super Bowl Sunday in the United States?

    a. 530 million
    b. 1.4 billion
    c. 752 million
    d. 1 billion

14. Are there more bourbon barrels in Kentucky than people?

    a. Yes
    b. No
    c. Unknown
    d. Kentucky has an equal number of bourbon barrels and people

15. What is the delectable state pie of Florida that was first made in the 1800s in the Florida Keys?

a. Lemon meringue pie

b. Shoo Fly pie

c. Key lime pie

d. Grapefruit pie

16. The popular Halloween candy, candy corn, used to be called "chicken feed."

    a. True

    b. False

17. What food do Americans deep fry and serve at public events such as state fairs?

    a. Deep-fried Oreos

    b. Deep-fried cheesecake

    c. Deep-fried Twinkies

    d. All of the above

18. What popular food/s do Americans eat every fall when the weather starts to get cool and the leaves change color?

    a. Pumpkins

    b. Apples

    c. Squash

    d. All of the above

19. In the Southern states, what food is considered to bring good luck and prosperity when eaten on New Year's Day?

    a. Collard greens

    b. Grits

    c. Fried okra

    d. Black-eyed peas

20. Which of the following is not a traditional American breakfast?

    a. Bagel with cream cheese

    b. Biscuits and gravy

    c. Macaroni and cheese

    d. Eggs and toast

ANSWER KEY

1. B- Beans, corn, and squash

2. B- Maple syrup

3. D- All of the above

4. C- Striking streetcar workers

5. B- Dr. John Harvey Kellogg

6. D- 100 acres

7. C- California

8. B- Le Mars, Iowa

9. D- Maine

10. A- Deep-dish

11. B- San Bernardino, California

12. B- S'mores

13. B- 1.4 billion

14. A- Yes

15. C- Key lime pie

16. A- True

17. D- All of the above

18. D- All of the above

19. D- Black-eyed peas

20. C- Macaroni and cheese

DID YOU KNOW?

1. Before the American Revolution, the inhabitants of New England drank large quantities of rum. Rum was the spirit of choice because trade with the West Indies provided the settlers with access to the main ingredient in rum, molasses.

2. Two United States presidents—Jimmy Carter and Thomas Jefferson—were peanut farmers.

3. In the 1790s, Thomas Jefferson brought a French waffle iron back to America and waffles became all the rage. Shortly after, the Pennsylvania Dutch population started putting chicken on top of waffles. Chicken and waffles have remained a popular American dish.

4. The potato chip was invented by George Crum, a Native American and African American chef in Saratoga Springs, New York. He worked in a diner and someone complained that the French fries were too thick: thus, the potato chip was invented.

5. Eggos, the popular frozen waffles created in California in the 1950s, used to be called "froffles" (for "frozen" + "waffles").

6. While many Americans believe that chili is a dish that originated from Mexico, it was born in the United States. Chili was invented in San Antonio, Texas in 1840. The first

chili was a combination of dried beef, beef fat, chili powder, and spices. It was pressed into a brick so it would not spoil quickly. Chili is now a staple dish in the United States, served with everything from hot dogs to cornbread.

7. Many people are familiar with American barbecue (BBQ), but what they do not realize is that BBQ in the United States is as diverse as the nation itself. All BBQ consists of meat and wood smoke, but the BBQ sauces and spices vary depending on the region. The BBQ in North Carolina and South Carolina is typically pork. It is traditionally rubbed with a spice mixture and eaten with a vinegar-based sauce, depending on the area of the Carolinas. It is the oldest form of American BBQ. Another style of BBQ is the Memphis style, which is typically ribs or BBQ sandwiches. Texas BBQ is another popular American dish and there are four different regions in Texas, all with their own style of BBQ.

8. A cheesesteak is a popular American sandwich made from thinly sliced beefsteak and cheese on a long roll. It originated in the city of Philadelphia, so cheesesteaks are often referred to as Philly cheesesteaks. Cheesesteaks are now typically served with either Cheez Whiz, American cheese, or provolone. Cheesesteaks are available throughout America in fast food type establishments, high-end restaurants, and as street food. Popular cheesesteak toppings include onions, peppers, mushrooms, and ketchup.

9. Tex-Mex, a fusion of Texan and Mexican, has become a staple across the country, particularly in the Southwestern United States. Some of the most loved Tex-Mex foods are tacos and enchiladas served with beef and yellow cheese instead of the typical white cheese served with Mexican food.

10. Believe it or not, in the state of Alaska, reindeer meat has been a staple since the 19th century. Alaskans love to eat this lean meat that is often served in the form of sausage or jerky.

CHAPTER 14

BIZARRE PRESIDENTIAL FACTS QUIZ

1. Two American presidents had alligators as pets that lived at the White House.

    a. True
    b. False

2. President William Howard Taft was so large he got stuck in his bathtub.

    a. True
    b. False

3. The deadliest job in the United States is being the president.

    a. True
    b. False

4. President Monroe was so dedicated to persuading the Spanish to cede what is now Florida to the United States that he traveled to Spain in 1805, and used what form of transportation to get from Paris to Madrid?

a. Train

b. Mule

c. Ostrich

d. Dog sled

5. Every single morning, this president would take a long walk and go skinny-dipping in the Potomac River before breakfast.

a. Thomas Jefferson

b. Abraham Lincoln

c. John Quincy Adams

d. James K. Polk

6. Which president regularly got into fights and actually killed a man in a duel for accusing him of cheating on a bet and then insulting his wife?

a. James Monroe

b. John C. Calhoun

c. George Washington

d. Andrew Jackson

7. Which president did not wear a coat to his inauguration, got sick, and died a month later?

a. William Henry Harrison

b. Rutherford B. Hayes

c. Calvin Coolidge

d. Martin Van Buren

8. Franklin Pierce, the 14th President of the United States, was arrested during his presidency for running over an

old lady with his horse. The case was dropped because there was not enough evidence.

a. True
b. False

9. Which president was ambidextrous and could write in Greek with one hand and in Latin with the other hand at the same time?

a. Grover Cleveland
b. Jimmy Carter
c. Bill Clinton
d. James Garfield

10. Which president worked as the sheriff of Erie County, NY and served as an executioner, hanging multiple men?

a. Grover Cleveland
b. Theodore Roosevelt
c. John F. Kennedy
d. Herbert Hoover

11. Which president was known for having a very dull presidency because he banned drinking, dancing, and card games in the White House during his time there?

a. Martin Van Buren
b. James Madison
c. James K. Polk
d. Gerald Ford

12. Which president is known as one of the heaviest drinkers that the office of the presidency has ever seen, once

stating to a friend when leaving office, "There is nothing left to do but get drunk"?

    a. Franklin Pierce

    b. Richard Nixon

    c. Harry Truman

    d. John Quincy Adams

13. Which president and his wife have been champions for the non-profit organization Habitat for Humanity for over 35 years?

    a. Bill Clinton and Hillary Clinton

    b. Jimmy Carter and Rosalynn Carter

    c. George Bush and Laura Bush

    d. Barack Obama and Michelle Obama

14. Who was the only lifelong bachelor to ever hold the office of the presidency?

    a. Herbert Hoover

    b. James Buchanan

    c. James Garfield

    d. Millard Fillmore

15. Franklin Delano Roosevelt and his wife, Eleanor, were blood relatives—specifically, fifth cousins once removed.

    a. True

    b. False

16. Which president donated his entire congressional and presidential salaries to charity?

    a. Harry Truman

b. John F. Kennedy

c. George W. Bush

d. Dwight D. Eisenhower

17. Which president worked as a model in college and was on the cover of the popular magazine, *Cosmopolitan,* in his naval uniform?

    a. John F. Kennedy

    b. Gerald Ford

    c. Harry Truman

    d. Barack Obama

18. Which African country named their capital, Monrovia, after James Monroe because he worked so hard to procure more United States funding for the American Colonization Society (ACS), which established the country?

    a. Liberia

    b. Ghana

    c. Democratic Republic of Congo

    d. Tanzania

19. James Monroe was a Virginia plantation owner and had slaves.

    a. True

    b. False

20. Barack Obama won two Grammys.

    a. True

    b. False

ANSWER KEY

1. A- True

2. B- False

3. A- True

4. B- Mule

5. C- John Quincy Adams

6. D- Andrew Jackson

7. A- William Henry Harrison

8. A- True

9. D- James Garfield

10. A- Grover Cleveland

11. C- James K. Polk

12. A- Franklin Pierce

13. B- Jimmy Carter and Rosalynn Carter

14. B- James Buchanan

15. A- True

16. B- John F. Kennedy

17. B- Gerald Ford

18. A- Liberia

19. A- True

20. A- True

DID YOU KNOW?

1. Many past presidents have been very wealthy and grew up in elite circles, but not all. Andrew Johnson was poor, and his mother sent him and his brother to work as indentured servants when they were just children. They later escaped. Johnson was taught to read and write by his wife, Eliza.

2. The first president to have electricity at the White House was Benjamin Harrison; however, he was too afraid to enjoy it. Harrison and his wife, Carolyn, were so nervous about electrocution that they were afraid to touch the light switches and left the lights on all day and night.

3. Theodore Roosevelt was shot by John Flammang Schrank on October 14, 1912, before his campaign speech in Milwaukee, where he was campaigning for an unprecedented third term in office. The bullet could have been fatal had it not gone through Roosevelt's 50-page folded speech manuscript and steel glasses case before it got to his body, where it penetrated his lung. Doctors wanted to immediately rush him to the hospital, but he refused and claimed that he needed to give his speech: which he did. During Roosevelt's epic speech, he showed the audience his bloody shirt and said, "It takes more than that to kill a bull moose." The incident gave Roosevelt a reputation, but he still lost the election.

4. As a child, Barack Obama lived in Indonesia and had a pet ape named "Tata."

5. George Washington grew large amounts of hemp at his home. Thomas Jefferson and James Madison also grew hemp. Although in the 1700s hemp was grown for its industrial value, it is believed that some founding fathers were aware of the effects of its counterpart, marijuana, and may have smoked it; however, this has not been proven.

6. In January 1992, George H.W. Bush attended a banquet hosted by the Prime Minister of Japan, Kiichi Miyazawa. At the banquet, Bush vomited on the prime minister's lap and then fainted. The vomiting incident was all over the media and was even satirized on an episode of *Saturday Night Live*, which depicted his wife, Barbara Bush, crawling across the table to get away.

7. President Calvin Coolidge thought it was good for his health to eat breakfast in bed while having petroleum jelly rubbed on his head.

8. Before becoming president, Jimmy Carter filed a report with the National Investigations Committee on Aerial Phenomena claiming that he saw an unidentified flying object (UFO) in 1969. While he was campaigning for the presidency, he did not deny it, stating that it was, "the darndest thing I've ever seen." One of his campaign promises was that, if he were elected, he would press for the federal government to release "every piece of information" about UFOs to the public.

9. The story that President Andrew Jackson's pet parrot cursed so much during the president's funeral that it had to be removed is true. A quote from the reverend who presided over the funeral states, "Before the sermon and while the crowd was gathering, a wicked parrot that was a household pet got excited and commenced swearing so loud and long as to disturb the people and had to be carried from the house."

10. After President John Tyler's death, he was so unpopular that in his obituary in the *New York Times* newspaper they called him "the most unpopular public man that had ever held any office in the United States."

CHAPTER 15

SPORTS IN AMERICA QUIZ

1. Which sport has been considered America's favorite pastime?

    a. Football
    b. Baseball
    c. Hockey
    d. Soccer

2. Which of the following statements about Muhammad Ali, America's famous boxer, is not true?

    a. He was sentenced for draft evasion during the Vietnam War
    b. He was in a Broadway musical
    c. He had roots in Ireland
    d. He never lost a match

3. How many World Series did Babe Ruth win in his 15 seasons with the New York Yankees?

    a. 3
    b. 4
    c. 7
    d. 9

4. While Michael Jordan played baseball, he was still getting paid to play basketball.

    a. True
    b. False

5. During World War II, so many football players from the NFL served in the military that, in 1943, the Philadelphia Eagles and the Pittsburgh Steelers had to combine their teams and call themselves the "Steagles."

    a. True
    b. False

6. Which team won the Super Bowl in 2018?

    a. New England Patriots
    b. Philadelphia Eagles
    c. Green Bay Packers
    d. Denver Broncos

7. Which two football teams have won the most Super Bowls, with six championship wins?

    a. Denver Broncos and the New England Patriots
    b. Green Bay Packers and the Dallas Cowboys
    c. Pittsburgh Steelers and the New England Patriots
    d. San Francisco 49ers and the Dallas Cowboys

8. Which two NFL teams have the oldest franchises?

    a. Chicago Bears and the Arizona Cardinals
    b. New York Giants and the New England Patriots
    c. Philadelphia Eagles and the Minnesota Vikings
    d. Buffalo Bills and the Cleveland Browns

9. Who is the youngest quarterback in NFL history to ever win a Super Bowl?

   a. Tom Brady
   b. Peyton Manning
   c. Ben Roethlisberger
   d. Russell Wilson

10. What is the only city in the United States where their NFL, NHL, and MLB teams all have the same colors?

    a. Philadelphia
    b. Pittsburgh
    c. Cleveland
    d. Boston

11. Umpires in Major League Baseball must wear black underwear during the games just in case they split their pants.

    a. True
    b. False

12. There have been two documented perfect March Madness brackets in history.

    a. True
    b. False

13. Even though, on average, Major League Baseball games last about three hours, there are only an estimated 18 minutes of action in a baseball game.

    a. True
    b. False

14. How old was Tiger Woods when he won the Junior World Golf Championship?

    a. 10 years old
    b. 15 years old
    c. 12 years old
    d. 8 years old

15. There are only ten quarterbacks in all of NFL history who have come close to throwing as many touchdown passes as Peyton Manning; and they have only thrown half as many as he did!

    a. True
    b. False

16. NFL referees also receive Super Bowl rings.

    a. True
    b. False

17. What speed can the average NASCAR car reach?

    a. 150 to 200 miles per hour
    b. 100 to 150 miles per hour
    c. 125 to 170 miles per hour
    d. 95 to 140 miles per hour

18. Which American athlete is the most decorated Olympic athlete in history?

    a. Jenny Thompson
    b. Nathan Adrian
    c. Michael Phelps
    d. Shaun White

19. At one stage, slam dunks were illegal in the National Basketball Association.

    a. True

    b. False

20. A volleyball was used to play basketball until 1929.

    a. True

    b. False

ANSWER KEY

1. B- Baseball

2. D- He never lost a match

3. B- 4

4. A- True

5. A- True

6. B- Philadelphia Eagles

7. C- Pittsburgh Steelers and the New England Patriots

8. A- Chicago Bears and the Arizona Cardinals

9. C- Ben Roethlisberger

10. B- Pittsburgh

11. A- True

12. B- False, there has never been a perfect bracket in March Madness history

13. A- True

14. D- 8 years old

15. B- False

16. A- True

17. A- 150 to 200 miles per hour

18. C- Michael Phelps

19. A- True

20. B- False, it was a soccer ball

DID YOU KNOW?

1. None of the baseballs that are used in Major League Baseball are clean and that choice is intentional. They purposely do not want to use new, slick baseballs because they want the pitchers to be able to get a good grip on the ball. The MLB rubs mud on each new baseball from a specific location on the Delaware River, which they have never disclosed. They have been practicing this odd ritual for 75 years.

2. Ray Caldwell, who was a pitcher for the Cleveland Indians, played out the rest of the game against the Philadelphia A's in 1919 after he was struck by lightning.

3. Babe Ruth used to wear a cabbage leaf under his baseball cap because he said it kept his body cool. He would change out the cabbage leaf for a fresh leaf every two innings.

4. The American tradition of baseball was officially born in 1846 when the New York Knickerbockers played the first game of baseball against a cricket team. One of the Knickerbockers' players, Alexander Joy Cartwright, created a set of rules that have become the foundation for modern baseball. His rules included the diamond-shaped infield, foul lines, and the "three strikes and you're out" rule.

5. The shortest basketball player to ever play in the NBA was Muggsy Bogues, at 5 feet and 3 inches.

6. There have been many talented basketball players who were drafted into the NBA straight out of high school, including LeBron James and Kobe Bryant. The NBA has now put a stop to drafting out of high school. It has been speculated that this ban is temporary, and the practice could return.

7. The popular winter sport of snowboarding was created in the United States in the 1960s, as a combination of skiing, skateboarding, sledding, and surfing. It officially became an Olympic Sport in 1998.

8. American Sherman Poppen is known as the "father of the snowboard" and created the prototype that evolved into the modern snowboard. He called it the "Snurfer," meaning "surfing on snow."

9. It takes 3,000 cows to supply the leather needed for the NFL footballs each year.

10. Pat Summitt, the University of Tennessee's women's basketball coach, retired with more wins than any other college sports coach in any sport. Under Summitt's leadership, the Lady Vols won eight national championships and had 1,098 wins, a record number of wins in major-college basketball history.

CHAPTER 16

THE STRANGE AND THE UNEXPLAINED QUIZ

1. Who was known as the "Wicked Witch of Monroe" for supposedly bewitching her husband and having him jump off a cliff in 19th century Connecticut?

    a. Bessie Smith
    b. Mary Thomas
    c. Hannah Cranna
    d. Sybil Leek

2. In Beebe, Arkansas, a small town in the United States, 5,000 blackbirds flew into buildings, telephone poles, and trees on New Year's Eve in 2010. The birds died instantly. The town attributed the deaths to fireworks that scared the birds and so, the next New Year's Eve, the town banned fireworks. The strange phenomenon happened again but with fewer birds.

    a. True
    b. False

3. Which prohibition-era gangster stashed an estimated $5–

$9 million-dollar treasure in the Catskill Mountains in New York State that has still not been found?

   a. Dutch Schultz

   b. Al Capone

   c. Al Pacino

   d. Legs Diamond

4. What is the name of the sculpture outside of the Central Intelligence Agency (CIA) headquarters in Langley, VA that contains four encrypted messages, fascinating people since its installation?

   a. Apocalypse

   b. The Symbol

   c. Kryptos

   d. Decipher

5. What is the name given to the unidentified serial killer who wreaked havoc on the San Francisco Bay area in the 1960s and 1970s and murdered at least seven victims, although the killer claims to have murdered 37?

   a. Cold Blood Killer

   b. Zodiac Killer

   c. Jack the Ripper

   d. Ted Bundy

6. Who was the American faith healer and cult leader who convinced his followers in the Peoples Temple cult to move to a community he created in Guyana and commit mass suicide by drinking cyanide-laced Flavor-Aid?

   a. Jim Jones

b. John Smith

c. Jessie Jones

d. Stephan Thomas

7. Bigfoot, a giant ape-like creature, is one of the most famous mysteries of all time. Bigfoot has been reportedly spotted in every state in the United States except _____.

a. Alaska

b. Hawaii

c. New York

d. Florida

8. Amelia Earhart, a pioneer in the aviation field, broke numerous records with her flying, making epic journeys like being the first woman to fly across the Atlantic in 1927. What became of Amelia Earhart?

a. She lived a long life in her home state of Kansas

b. She crashed her plane in the United States desert and her remains were never found

c. She was last seen departing from Papua New Guinea with her navigator, Fred Noonan, while trying to make a record-breaking flight around the world

d. After she made her last record-breaking flight around the world, she decided to retire

9. In which United States city did the famous Unidentified Flying Object (UFO) incident take place in 1947, in which a rancher discovered debris in his pastures, such as

chunks of plastic and metallic rods, which he and the media deemed to be a flying saucer that had crashed?

   a. Austin, Texas

   b. Roswell, New Mexico

   c. Flemington, New Jersey

   d. Palo Alto, California

10. Which United States president's ghost has been reportedly seen by White House staff, guests, and residents for the past century?

   a. George Washington

   b. Franklin D. Roosevelt

   c. Abraham Lincoln

   d. Calvin Coolidge

11. One week after the assassination of President John F. Kennedy, President Lyndon B. Johnson created a commission to investigate his death. What was the name of this commission that is still being called into question today?

   a. The JFK Commission

   b. The Warren Commission

   c. The Oswald Commission

   d. The Presidential Safety Investigation Commission

12. Who was the New Orleans woman known as the "Queen of Voodoo", who was a practitioner of voodoo and an herbalist, telling fortunes, creating potions, and healing the sick?

a. Marie Laveau

b. Tituba

c. Queen Bianca

d. Ava Kay Jones

13. Which famous hip-hop star was killed in a drive-by shooting in Las Vegas in 1996 that was never solved?

a. The Notorious B.I.G.

b. Fat Pat

c. Paul C.

d. Tupac Shakur

14. What was the name of the girl who was accused of murdering her father and stepmother in Connecticut in 1892 in a case that still captivates the public?

a. Lizzie Borden

b. Elizabeth Gordan

c. Andrea Yates

d. Evelyn Dick

15. What is Area 51?

a. A place where the United States stores alien bodies

b. A classified United States Air Force facility in Nevada that is used as a training range

c. An area that is now uninhabitable because the United States government tested a bomb there

d. A secret United States government facility that no one is allowed to enter, not even members of the United States military

16. There is an urban legend in Virginia about the Bunny Man, who is supposedly a former insane asylum patient who dresses in a giant bunny suit and scares away trespassers with an ax.

    a. True
    b. False

17. What is the name of the supposedly haunted tunnels in Portland, Oregon that were used in the 19th century to hold men who had been kidnapped and drugged, and were later sold at the waterfront as unpaid laborers?

    a. Shanghai Tunnels
    b. Cascade Tunnels
    c. Poltergeist Tunnels
    d. Terror Tunnels

18. What is the name of the infamous bridge in Alabama where, according to urban legend, if you look over your shoulder while you drive over the bridge, you will see a portal to hell, surrounded by flames?

    a. Devil's Bridge
    b. Bridge to Hell
    c. Hell's Gate Bridge
    d. Bridge of No Return

19. There have been reported sightings of a 30-foot-long sea monster named "Chessie" in the Chesapeake Bay.

    a. True
    b. False

20. The grave of Lilly E. Gray, who was buried in the Salt Lake City Cemetery in 1858, mysteriously states that she was the...

    a. "Victim of the beast 666"

    b. "Victim of a vampire"

    c. "Worshipper of the devil himself"

    d. "A witch who committed numerous evils"

ANSWER KEY

1. C- Hannah Cranna

2. A- True

3. A- Dutch Schultz

4. C- Kryptos

5. B- Zodiac Killer

6. A- Jim Jones

7. B- Hawaii

8. C- She was last seen departing from Papua New Guinea with her navigator, Fred Noonan, while trying to make a record-breaking flight around the world

9. B- Roswell, New Mexico

10. C- Abraham Lincoln

11. B- The Warren Commission

12. A- Marie Laveau

13. Tupac Shakur

14. A- Lizzie Borden

15. B- A classified United States Air Force facility in Nevada that is used as a training range

16. A- True

17. A- Shanghai Tunnels

18. C- Hell's Gate Bridge

19. A- True

20. "Victim of the beast 666"

DID YOU KNOW?

1. Alcatraz, one of the United States' most notorious prisons, located on the isolated Alcatraz Island in San Francisco, California, saw 14 escape attempts by 36 men in total. Almost all of them were caught or did not survive; all except for three inmates.

   On June 12, 1962, John Anglin, his brother Clarence, and Frank Morris were not in their beds. In place of the inmates were dummy heads made of plaster. The dummies were made so cleverly—the inmates even used real human hair—that the night guards were fooled. The men were not discovered to be missing until the morning.

   To this day, the men have never been found. Authorities at the time concluded that the men did not survive, but many have tried to prove that the men could have survived. Did they? To this day, no one knows.

2. In 1947, aspiring actress Elizabeth Short was brutally murdered in Los Angeles. The killer cut her body in half and drained her of all her blood. The horrific murder that remains unsolved has captivated the American public, and the case has been made into many books and films.

3. In 1990, the world's biggest unsolved art robbery took place in Boston at the Isabella Stewart Gardner Museum. Two thieves disguised themselves as police officers and

the security guards believed them. They duped the guards and put them in handcuffs while they stole 13 paintings. The thieves made it out with a haul worth an estimated $500 million, including famous paintings like a Rembrandt and a Vermeer. There are still not any significant leads as to who carried out the art heist.

4. In 1971, a man hijacked a plane traveling from Oregon to Seattle. Once the plane arrived in Seattle, he freed the 36 passengers on the plane in exchange for ransom money to the amount of $200,000 and four parachutes. After the flight took off from Seattle, the hijacker—who went by the name of Dan Cooper—asked the pilots to fly the plane incredibly low en route to Mexico City. During the flight, Cooper jumped out of the plane with his parachute and money and was never seen again.

   Other than the fact that the man called himself Dan Cooper, not much else is known about him, despite the FBI investigating hundreds of dead-end leads. In 2016, the FBI officially announced they were no longer pursuing the hijacker, after 45 years of a long and fruitless search.

5. A floating light appears above a railroad track in the town of Gurdon, Arkansas, each October. The light has been reported since the 1930s and thousands of people have seen it. The cause of the light is still unknown. Some theorize that the light is the ghost of a railroad worker who was murdered, while others have a more scientific explanation, attributing it to a natural occurrence caused by rock quartz underneath the land.

6. In April 1941, in Odon, Indiana, a series of unexplained fires plagued the home of a local family. In total, 28 fires were extinguished, one after another, with no apparent cause. After blaming a poltergeist for the fires, the family tore down the entire house, built a new one, and never had another fire again.

7. In 1942, the residents of Pascagoula, Mississippi were plagued by an alleged phantom who would go around slitting window screens, sneaking into people's houses, and cutting their hair, particularly the hair of blonde girls.

8. The Hoosac Tunnel, nicknamed "The Bloody Pit," claimed the lives of 200 men during its construction. A particularly grisly death was that of 13 miners who got trapped in the tunnel, built a raft to escape the flooding, but still died from inhaling poisonous gas. Legend has it that the tunnel is now haunted by these 13 men.

9. One of the most infamous vampire legends of the city of New Orleans is that of Jacque St. Germain, an attractive, extremely wealthy, mysterious man. He claimed to be a direct descendent of the Comte de St. Germain, a well-known 18th-century figure, but after seeing the astounding resemblance of the two, New Orleans residents began to claim that Jacque St. Germain was immortal and was the Comte de St. Germain himself.

   After one of Jacque St. Germain's parties, a woman jumped off his balcony trying to escape Germain, claiming that he bit her neck. After the incident, he vanished, leaving his belongings behind, and was never seen again.

10. Following a classic urban legend, children in the United States play a popular game during sleepovers where they go into a dark room with a mirror and repeat the words "Bloody Mary" three times. Legend has it that, if you do so, you will see Mary Tudor's ghost.

CONCLUSION

The United States of America has a rich history, filled with brilliant inventions, democratic principles, devastating wars, fights for equality, and resilient people. Women, African Americans, and other minority populations have made many gains for themselves since the founding of the United States of America, but the country is still far from equal. There is a lot to be done in the fight for equality for many.

What makes the United States so unique is that it is indeed a melting pot, and since its inception it has been the home of immigrants. The diverse population that makes up the country has contributed to the United States' delicious food, internationally renowned music, and unique traditions. With the celebration of everything from St. Patrick's Day to Groundhog Day, there are many holidays to be enjoyed in a uniquely American way.

In addition to their love of music and food, Americans have always enjoyed good films. Hollywood still dominates the world film industry, and American culture loves to stay up to date on the lives of its celebrities. From movie stars to famous sports players, America has plenty, and their exciting lives continue to captivate audiences not just in the States but across the globe.

The United States is a vast country with a rich history and culture. This book has hopefully taught you a lot of new trivia knowledge you can use to impress your friends and enlighten them about critical historical events. Remember, there is always so much more to learn. Be sure to look out for our other trivia books and continue your path of lifelong learning.

DON'T FORGET YOUR FREE BOOKS

MORE BOOKS BY BILL O'NEILL

I hope you enjoyed this book and learned
something new. Please feel free to check
out some of my previous books on **Amazon**.